GRACE NOTES AND BAD THOUGHTS

JOHN KELLY

JOHN KELLY was born in Enniskillen in 1965. His poetry has been published by The Blackstaff Press and his readings have taken him to venues all over Ireland, Britain and the United States. He lives in Belfast and works as a freelance writer and broadcaster. This is his first novel.

First published in 1994 by
Martello Books
An imprint of Mercier Press
16 Hume Street Dublin 2

Trade enquiries to Mercier Press
PO Box 5, 5 French Church Street,
Cork

A Martello Original

© John Kelly 1994

ISBN 1 86023 003 2

10 9 8 7 6 5 4 3 2 1

A CIP record for this title is available
from the British Library

Cover design by Brian Finnegan
Set by Richard Parfrey in Avant
Garde and Caslon Regular 10/14
Printed by ColourBooks, Baldoyle
Industrial Estate, Dublin 13

References on pp. 39–40, 133–4 and 144
are to Francis O'Neill's *Irish Minstrels and
Musicians* (first pub. 1913).

IN MEMORY OF FRANKIE KENNEDY

ONE

Of a man's first disobedience there is much to be said — and perhaps the best place to start is the day I boked all over Joseph Haverty's 'The Blind Piper' in the National Gallery of Ireland. It was one of those sudden bokes that catches the boker completely by surprise — if I'd had even the slightest indication that such a Vesuvian boke was on the cards I would not have been standing in front of Joseph Haverty's 'Blind Piper' with my mouth open. It stands to sense.

Like a sudden and violent dig in the ribs, it was a sharp elbow in the very cage itself. Clutching at my side with both hands, I doubled over with the kidney pain of the whole affair and out came a terrific rush of air — expelled with such a hellish force that out with it came the mother of all bokes — a ferocious geyser of a crop-spraying and psychedelic boke. A hurl. A barf. A puke. A throw. And that, as the man says, was the start of it.

The reason I was positioned where I was (with my mouth open) at the time of my unfortunate accident is worth noting at this early stage. The National Gallery of Ireland is a grand building with its own front garden in Merrion Square West, Dublin 2. In keeping with the art gallery concept worldwide it houses a fine collection of works of art offered up for public edification and delight. Jack Yeats, Picasso, Caravaggio and Sir John Lavery make it a day well spent although, rather foolishly in my opinion, the gallery remains closed until two o'clock of a Sunday – just the sort of time a man with a hangover might be at a loose end and in need of easy amusement. Paintings, sculptures and fine staircases apart, one can also take pleasure from tea, buns, assorted snacks and the sight of poets tripping others. It is a wonderful place altogether. The height of good taste.

My favourite work in the National Gallery of Ireland is 'The Blind Piper' by Joseph Haverty (1794-1864). It is a fine representation in oils and is also available in postcard format from the well-stocked Gallery Shop priced at around sixty gleaming red Irish pennies. A blind man wearing possibly only the one sock is playing on a set of union or uilleann pipes and appears to sit without the aid of a chair or other visible means of support. His companion is a small, sad-faced, barefoot girl who is toasting her toes by a miserable fire and knows much more than she is letting on. It is a peculiar picture – neither happy nor sad and the juxtaposition of the two figures is unnerving. The tune being played is, I suspect, 'The Wind that Shakes the Barley'.

Joseph Haverty's 'Blind Piper' is my all-time, fave-rave *objet d'art* and is doubtless a credit to the nation. My reasons for being fornenst it were complex and sinister and all I am prepared to reveal at this stage in my meander is that I suffered at the time from a condition which amounted to an unnatural perverted perversion and an unshakeable obsessional obsession with the sweet elbow pipes. I loved the look of the pipes, the feel of the pipes, the mechanics of the pipes, the flawless poetry of their design and above all I adored the delicate noises they produced. While all my schoolfriends were banging their heads to The Undertones and Tom Robinson, I could hear it high up in the air, a piper piping away. I heard the music in the wind, in the sally bushes and on old 78s – Willie Clancy, Seamus Ennis, Felix Doran and the greatest of them all – the ace and deuce – the man they called Liam Óg Ó Floinn. Young Willie Flynn was my hero! He was like a god! I sat at his feet and wept.

If I was to go back just a little further I might be fit to begin with another beginning – but how can a man ever put his finger on such a thing? How can I say with any certainty on what exact day things began to happen in the way that they did? At what precise moment in time and space did this nightmare begin? the slide, the fall – the sad decay that first manifested itself in that gut-twisting hurl in the National Gallery of Ireland. Was there a single, unique moment in history when I first staggered off the path and took to the wet fields of sin? I have a fair idea – so I have.

Fadó, fadó. The last day of May, Nineteen Hundred and Eighty Two. I purchased for my own pleasure Twenty Regal Kingsize and a Planxty cassette called *The Woman I Loved So Well.* I smoked the cigarettes one after another like that fella in *A Bout De Souffle,* caring not a jot where I threw the butt and perhaps it was that first drag on that first dizzying fag that was the start of it – it was certainly the beginning of something. The Alpha. The Omphalos. The Boa Island.

The pack of twenty was followed by a manly-voiced order for twelve pints of stout. They arrived on two trays and were set before me – their heads a flowerfield of creamy shamrocks and smiling faces. I named each one after an apostle and commenced to wallop them into me. By the time I had downed Bartholomew I was as full as a sheugh – by the second James as full as a bingo bus. Half-way down Judas I began to weep rather endearingly at the thought of Liam Óg Ó Floinn playing something slow. Peter, Andrew, James and John. Philip, Bartholomew, Matthew, Thomas. Simon, James, Jude and Judas.

This virginal boozing caused chaos in both brain and bladder and during one of my not infrequent visits to the toilets I encountered yet another epiphanic experience. A large Wagnerian woman clearly identifiable as a tourist by reason of her yellow wellingtons, commenced a stilted, angular conversation:

My yellow vellinktonbutts . . . you like?

Yella wellies? They're the cat's pajamas!

Our conversation was short and quite senseless, inspired as it was by complete drunkenness and muddied further by language difficulties and an alarming burgeoning lust. She took me to her cruiser where we drank tequila slammers and became as full as forty badgers. I told her about Liam Ó Floinn and insisted that she listen to my new cassette – Ó Floinn playing on a set of reels – 'The Woman I Never Forgot', 'The Pullet' and 'The Ladies' Pantalettes'.

She kept me up half the night as the grey monastic waters of the Erne gently lapped against the side of the cruiser and the cruiser, in its turn, creaked against the ragged half-tyres nailed to jetty. The jetty itself fairly swayed. Oh Catholic guilt where are you!

She had loose morals and a tight duvet and she introduced me, among other things, to a revelatory cigarette which she had carried with her all the way from Baden-Baden. All of the above came together, stirred lightly by the gentle rocking of the boat, to create a most delicious, simmering feeling of well-being. In the morning I was seasick and I boked on the bank.

All of this, horrifically, on my seventeenth birthday! From being a fully pledged member of the Pioneer and Total

Abstinence Association, the Legion of Mary, CBSI, Youth Together, the Junior Orange Lodge, Saint Vincent de Paul and the Planxty Fan Club I became overnight a gauge-smoking, liquor-swilling, womanising, hedonistic and decadent Lothario and I must say that I felt much happier in myself.

As I wandered home through the dewy fields of meadow-sweet and Piper orchids the yellow-billed blackbirds were in full swagger. Shivering to the melodious calls of the corncrake I thrilled to the gentle roll of the bream in the deepest of glarry pools. It was a beautiful, still, glasscalm Fermanagh morning and I lilted three tunes – 'The Woman I Never Forgot', 'The Pullet' and 'The Ladies' Pantalettes'.

Author's Note

I have on several occasions employed the word 'boke' and I have this long time advocated its use. Although not listed in the *Concise Oxford Dictionary* it is undoubtedly one of our linguistic treasures – a noun, a verb and *in extremis* a term of abuse. It is a bloody marvellous, evocative, and, to top it all, onomatopoeic word. Where would you get it?

Its origins lie in the Latin *boccere* meaning to erupt and its volcanic root was later adapted by Irish missionaries to mean vomit, spew or puke. 'One good boke and you'll be right as rain' is a piece of reassurance commonly heard in the men's toilets of your typical public house. (It is incidentally a proven medical fact that a good boke can indeed be as good as a tonic.)

The word also possesses unfathomable comic possibilities: a boke at bedtime; to throw the boke at someone; I see Cantona was boked on Saturday etc.

End of Author's Note

Having performed variations on the *Ring Cycle* with my tourist companion and having been introduced to the joys of booze, fags, recreational drugs of all sorts and of course the comfort that is to be had from members of the opposite sex, I was under something of a durundive obligation to get the hell out of school. A single-sex institution full of single boys who were singularly encouraged to play shirtless Gaelic football during hailstorms on an all-weather pitch was no longer the place for me. Typical of the deceit, the all-weather pitch had only one kind of weather.

Of course many of my classmates were already on the wrong tarmac – smoking Woodbines, Regal, Benson and Hedges and Capstan Full Strength behind the handball alleys – a venue also used for scraps or brawls where two unfortunate specimens were goaded into gladiatorial combat for the Roman throng: *Come-on Pa-dee! Come-on Pa-dee!* Other boys certainly drank. Big hallions from the country would be out gargling *poitín* from all hours and knew well that a glass of water the next morning would set themselves drunk again. This was a common enough procedure and manys an O-level English exam was passed by a very creative and totally plastered young man

What I'm saying is this. Plenty of boys smoked, plenty drank and some may even have witnessed a spliff being passed around when Thin Lizzy played at the RDS. Certainly some of the boys had girlfriends and told colourful lies about them – but none of them had done what I had done! The whole shooting match! In the one go! On a boat! I felt obliged to leave school that very afternoon – just as Father Monaghan handed out copies of the June issue of *Reality* – a Redemptorist publication with an outrageous misnomer.

I disappeared for two or three years and eventually ended

up in New York – hanging around Manhattan with people like myself – all of us dedicated to the relentless pursuit of pleasure in whatever form it came – drinking, smoking, snorting, brawling, toilet-sleeping, gutter-crawling, women-chasing and knocking on Woody Allen's door and running away. I was arrested many times and as you will discover spent manys an hour of self-discovery in a NYPD cage. Who loves ya baby?

Throughout this misremembered period of my life my obsession with the pipes remained and I took every opportunity to strap on bellows and bag. In the midst of chaos and nightmare there was always one figure who represented all that was decent and true and that was Liam Óg Ó Floinn. A solid man. I hung his picture over the bed and thought little else of home save the sweet lamentations of the pipes and the gentle creaking of cruiser-boats on the clear moonlit waters of the Erne. The winding banks. My watery home.

TWO

St Augustine was a terrible man. And I say that with all due respect. Like myself, he was born and reared on a farm and was conversant with all manner of goats, chickens and rare breeds. He could handle a spade and specialised in the ancient Irish loy and manys an evening he would sit on the hills overlooking Thagaste listening to the sweet call of the yellow bittern and saying his prayers.

Eastern Algeria differed to some degree from my own stonewalled acres and hanging hills but myself and Augustine shared many things – not least a tardy conscience. He taught literature in Rome, Milan and Carthage, and as you will discover later I too have had my moments in these places. He footered about with all manner of thought including theosophy, scepticism and Neoplatonist mysticism. I for my part used to run about with Van Morrison.

For the purposes of my current contemplations I find great solace in the writings of Augustine. Having sowed his wild oats with heterosexual abandon, only at the very last minute did he pray for a crop failure. He gallivanted around town – drinking, smoking, snorting, brawling, toilet-sleeping, gutter-crawling, woman-chasing and knocking the door of the Carthaginian equivalent of Woody Allen and running like the bejapers. A tearaway without equal and a quare cowboy of outrageous dimensions, he ran like the wind through the shadowy jungle of erotic adventures – the very same jungle in which I myself would one day be lost without map, compass or bearings.

What binds me ever closer to my fourth-century friend is that we were both blessed with Irish mothers. Our maters stormed heaven on a daily basis and lit candles to beat the band. Even at the vilest points of our respective evil existences our furrow-browed mothers were at the backs of our minds. Some day (but not right now) we would get off our trains and return penitent and à pied to the faith of our mothers and a moral life, an ordered universe and a God who was good.

At such moments however I always found that a half bottle of Ol' Grandad Kentucky Bourbon 101 proof would put such notions of crisis out of my head. These were my lost moments – my moments of absolute faithlessness and degradation – moments when even my own saintly mother might have abandoned all hope and temporarily suspended her perpetual novena.

As you are probably aware by now I am postponing the moment when I actually confront in open and honest exposé the horrors I have endured and perpetrated. What you have heard so far is nothing and cannot hold a candle to what follows. This is a tale of moral decay and it is in its own way a moral tale. It is, at first, the story of one young man who came from a good home and loved the squeeze of the uilleann pipes. Without delay it becomes the story of a shocking altogether saga of murder, deceit, the ancient people of Ireland, necromantic constraint and a neo-Faustian quest for 'The Woman I Never Forgot', 'The Pullet' and 'The Ladies' Pantalettes'. Bear with me.

The Greeks have the cheek to give the *douze* points to the Cypriots. The Cypriots reciprocate. They do that every year! Bloody Greeks! Bloody Cypriots! Bloody Freaks and Apricots! Terry raises an eyebrow – all of it old alliances and old enemies. The Armada! The Year of the French! The wind rising in the channel! Old axes – old axis – to grind.

Bosnia Herzegovinia get an ovation for showing up. *Royaume Uni* are dreary as hell and virtually pointless. Hungary get off to a flier and Ryan is up to high doh – wearing a yellow jacket and shouting like Mussolini:

'Did yis ever in your shaggin' lives see anything like that! I mean ever! Did yis ever see anything as fuckin' brilliant! I mean seriously, lads! Wasn't that just the bee's knees!'

And isn't Cynthia just gorgeous? Niamh of the Golden Hair – taking no shite from anybody and talking languages like they were going out of fashion – a beautiful golden haired polyglot of a princess taking the whole of Europe to *Tir na nÓg* on the back of her horse. Ireland twelve points – *Irlande douze points!*

Wrap the Green Flag Round Me Boys! says Terry. Isn't the Emerald Isle one serious happening place! A very young population, the president is a woman, the football team can beat anybody with their hands tied behind their backs and the Eurovision in a cakewalk. (Mind you the North is a ballocks.)

What I'm getting around to is this. Did you see what I saw? Slap bang in the middle of one of those Bord Fáilte Discover Ireland's Green and Pleasant Land *Quiet Man* videos there it was! In the midst of all that Olé Olé Olé and this is for Drumshanbo – there was the National Gallery of Ireland, Merrion Square West, Dublin 2! Caravaggio and Jack Yeats and yes! Joseph Haverty's 'The Blind Piper' as large as life and all cleaned up. 'That's the Blind Piper,' says Terry and indeed and it was. I felt my jaws twitch.

End of Author's Note

How's your ma? asks Augustine sitting down and arranging his fine robe about his legs.

Ah workin' away there, says I, doing novenas and lighting the candles. How's your ma?

On her two knees as usual.

Many years ago the two of us would sit on a reasonable class of a hill or mound and look out across the wet whinbushes of Fermanagh – to be precise the townlands of Derrygore, Drumgay, Kilmacormack, Derrychara and Cornagrade. Heavy bruisy clouds would gather in from Tyrone and Augustine would say that it was a wet oul day.

Wet oul day, says Augustine.

Aye surely, says I.

Better than the oul sun anyway, says he, examining his toes which reared rather unpleasantly from his sandals, I don't like the good weather.

Do you not?

I do not.

Augustine had strange notions about things and had no interest whatever in association football, rounders or trying to do handstands. There was no harm in him but he could be weird company.

You see them evenings, says he, when the sun does be out and it does be good drying weather? You know them evenings when you can smell the cut grass and there does be midges and corncrakes all over the place. Them evenings are bad evenings.

You mean, says I confused, them summer evenings when

the blackbird does be singing and the swallows do be flying and the snipe does be drumming?

I do hate them evenings.

Do you?

I do.

And why so? says I.

Ah, says he with a sigh, the place does be trippin' with women in printed cotton dresses and them with their bare arms flailing about the place. You couldn't be up to women in sleeveless printed cotton dresses on warm evenings like that.

Looking back now on our almost nightly conversations it is clear that I had no idea of what my zealous Algerian friend spoke – not a baldie's notion. Clouds of muddy carnal concupisence no less! Precipitous rocks of desire! Whirlpools of vice!

You must understand that, in my pre-pubescent innocence, I had no idea about the life he had led before the mother got him home and started feeding him the apple tart. Back then, at a time when all I desired was a pair of real football boots and a Chopper, how could I ever have understood and foreseen that one day I myself, like Augustine, would be rolling in the streets of Babylon.

I was only eleven years old. In September I would, for the first time, put on a school uniform, pierce my lapel with a Pioneer Pin and go to the big boys' school. There I would learn about science and how to talk French and Irish. I would have to study hard every night and in the end I would be a fine young man who would read the lesson on Sundays and visit the sick. I would be upright, respectable and good living – far from pool-hall, public house and street corner. I would wear a patterned jumper stuffed inside my cords – and a nice wee suede belt.

I had always been a model child.

Ah he's very good, people would say with a grin, you're very good aren't you?

And they were right. I never lifted my foot to anyone, threw stones, broke windows, wrote on desks, took drags on fags, snook nips from bottles, pulled pigtails, said bad words, picked fights, let down tyres, robbed orchards or tortured animals. I was gleaming and pure like that picture of Ignatius Loyola – in a permanent state of post-confessional grace.

This was, of course, a completely unnatural condition which brought with it almost unbearable pressures. Once people around me began to believe that I was inherently good they were forgetting one vital and often ignored reality, i. e. that we are all inherently evil. Nevertheless having been declared a good child, I could not under any circumstances be a bad child. I could not in all conscience let anybody down – parents, aunts, grandparents, nuns in the first class or, for that matter, nuns in my mother's first class. Their disappointment would be too great and the shock too severe. Standards had been set and it mattered not that those standards were inhuman – nor did it matter that I, in my ignorance of life, I had set those standards for myself. My failure was unthinkable and yet, at the same time, inevitable.

I often imagined with horror the worst case scenario:

'This young man has been found while scheming school. He had secreted himself in the rushes and was smoking like a Trojan on single loose shoplifted Woodbines and munching away like Adam himself on an orchard apple!'

Such were the imagined limits of my badness in those pre-lapsarian days before I had discovered that my wholesomeness was unreal – in fact a sin against nature and that I was *de facto* bad. Before I caught myself on. Before I twigged that Augustine was right – and so was his mother.

THREE

P addy Roberts taught English and had no obvious redeeming features. He was a southpaw and I hated the man with an almost evil intensity. If such a thing can be imagined I think it is fair to say that he resembled a ferocious wombat in a bad suit and I think it also fair to say that he was a psychopath of the highest order.

Roberts was completely offensive and malignant in every way and appeared to take great pride in his condition. Given to persistent and brutal violence he usually prefaced each attack with some colourfully expressed hint as to his intentions: *They'll be scraping you off the back of that wall for the rest of the week with a very thin scalpel!* or *I'll put my fist so far down your throat that they'll be picking your teeth out of your shite!* – most unsavoury expressions I'm sure you'll agree.

These remarkable and imaginative turns of phrase did however appear to mark the borders of his literary sensibilities. Shakespeare for example was used exclusively as an excuse to perpetrate acts of unspeakable violence – failure to react in the appropriate manner to a particular speech would result in a sharp left uppercut to the jaw and a re-enactment of whatever scene of torture or eye-gouging that had stumped the unfortunate pupil in the first place.

His other delight was the spelling test – a daily ritualistic torture where each boy would be requested to stand up and spell words plucked at random from Paddy Roberts's twisted mind –

Solzhenitsyn! Electroencephelographically!

Your certain deficiencies would be rewarded with an abrupt knee to the groin followed by a class of karate chop to the nape of the neck. The victim was, under no circumstances, to make a loud noise or defend himself in any way. This might well lead to expulsion.

On this particular drizzling morning as I looked wistfully out the window and admired the petrol sheen from the criminally underrated plumage of a magpie I was interrupted by the demonic gulders of Paddy Roberts:

Hey big ears! Spell ballocks!

Pardon sir?

Are you deaf as well as stupid?

No sir?

Spell ballocks! he screamed.

I stood up with little hope in my heart –

B-A-L-L-O-C-K-S?

Ha! blurted Roberts, Incorrect!

B-A-L-L . . . O-C-K-S?

Incorrect! Incorrect! B-A-L-L what?

O-C-K-S?

Are you retarded, boy?

I don't know?

I tried again –

B-A-L-L-O-C-K-S?

Paddy Roberts turned to the blackboard wearing his exasperated expression. Slowly he printed in a childish hand:

B-A-L-L-O-X.

B, he groaned, A-L-L-O-X!

With a modicum of calm he replaced the chalk in his dusty tobacco tin and began to roll up his sleeves. He looked particularly ugly — all lardy-faced and covered in chalkdust and dandruff.

Right Dumbo! he squealed, get out here!

He began to shadowbox.

Sir, I mumbled, I think you can spell it both ways . . . I mean if you . . .

He leapt forward and planted his forehead right on the bridge of my nose. I heard a crunch and a ring and felt an awful hot wetness as I staggered back against my desk — upending it and taking with it the next boy and the next. I touched the liquid warmth on my face and watched a steady flow of blood begin a rich Jackson Pollock on the polished wooden floor. I heard someone gasp: he's busted his nose!

I felt sick and looking up I saw three Paddy Roberts still shadowboxing away to themselves. If it had been an animated feature, a selection of tweeting birds would have been in orbit around my head — as this was animated bloody reality demons flew out of my nostrils like bats out of hell.

Right Roberts you fat fucker! You want to fight? The box alley! Now!

Word was beaten out on lime green radiators and within minutes bells were ringing and schemers were returning from the fields. Staff and pupils gathered noisily at the handball alleys and jostled for prime position. The Morrigu and Badb, the great crows of battle began to circle overhead.

I pushed my way into the box alley and looked around at all the faces leering over at me. All the teachers were there in their bad suits and all the priests too — all taking bets and chanting for their man. A messenger was dispatched to inform the bishop.

The youths had all removed their ties and had knotted them around their heads in accordance with local ritual and some brazenly lit up and took deep, grave drags. This, we all knew, was the first time a pupil had challenged a teacher to a fight – any teacher – let alone Paddy Roberts. As for the challenger – he had never been in a fight in his life. Couldn't box eggs.

Such traumas are, however, great moments of self discovery. Already I had learned that there was a point where I was no longer prepared to be perfection itself – a point where regardless of letting myself or anyone else down I would take the necessary action. There was a point where I would stand up for myself and a point where I would with great freedom use the f-word. It was a point where no other word would do.

I had also discovered that I was tougher, braver and a damn sight more impressive than I thought I was – a side of myself up to that moment denied. Perhaps even more significantly (and this might seem like a strange concept to introduce all of a sudden) I discovered that I was descended directly from the ancient people of Ireland – The Tuatha Dé Danaan. Get your head around that one!

Author's Note

The Tuatha Dé Danaan or the Tribe of Danu are a semi-divine race of people who inhabit Ireland. Many centuries ago they ruled the land after defeating the Formorians – giants, hard cases and heavy drinkers. The Tuatha Dé Danaan were in the end beaten themselves by the fearsome Milesians and went underground to live in the many raths or *síthe* that are to be found all over the country. All of these battles and capers took place in Fermanagh.

The tales of the Tuatha Dé Danaan are to be found in the

great Ulster Cycle – ancient tales of heroes and heroic feats. The greatest hero of them all was Cuchulainn – The Hound of Ulster. (Gentiles may need to be reminded that the Ulster Cycle was not some class of Unionist velocipede like, for instance, an Ulster-Says-No Raleigh and also that Cuchulainn was no more a dog than I am myself.)

The Hound of Ulster's father was named Lú and his mother was named Macha – both of the Tuatha Dé Danaan. Their son, then called Setanta, possessed many great gifts and grew up to be famous throughout the four provinces for his skills at chess-playing, hurley-flinging, dog-killing, spear-throwing, ball-catching, goal-scoring, badger-baiting, fly-tying, hare-coursing, paint-stripping, fence-balancing, book-binding, egg-juggling, hornpipe-dancing, sword-rattling, chariot-racing, poetry-saying, story-telling, song-singing, speech-making, joy-riding, wine-tasting, woman-kissing, handball-playing, deer-stalking, sleep-walking, water-swimming, earth-hoking, crop-spraying, mountain-hopping, buck-lepping, tune-lilting, time-wasting, skittle-throwing, blackberry-picking, pipe-squeezing, boat-rowing, hair-curling, javelin-swallowing, weight-lifting, pole-vaulting, ball-kicking and ferret-fancying.

He was the greatest hero of all Ireland and in full battle frenzy he would slay a thousand men with the one smack. His eyes would bulge and his hair would stand on end. His whole face would contort, his body would assume many grotesque forms and a hero-light would shine about his head. In this state he would think nothing of beating the entrails out of a thousand fearsome warriors with the little finger of his left hand with his other hand tied behind his back. This magical transformation into battle frenzy was known as warp spasm.
End of Author's Note

Paddy Roberts appeared with his shirt off. He wore a vest and possessed gruesome hairy shoulders. His face was like a Quattro Stagioni pizza.

Come on Pa-dee! Come-on Pa-dee! rose the moronic chant from the teaching staff.

Wombat is a wanker! sang the boys.

Roberts stepped forwards, his fat face full of evil and his rubbery mouth full of drool. He landed a straight forearm shove on my shoulder and I staggered back. He pushed me again –

Right wingnut! I'll teach you your spellings! He pushed again and shouted B! another shove and A! a shoulder this time and L! a dunt and L! a punch to the left eye and O! and finally a humiliating slap on the ear and X!

How do you spell it, Dumbo? Eh? What?

All I remember is taking a wild look around me at all the faces and the furious exchange of money among priests and teachers. All else is a tad hazy. For a complete understanding of what happened I refer you to the note above. My face began to contort and my hair stood on end. My eyes bulged and my body began to assume grotesque and fearsome forms. A hero-light shone about my head. The box alley was filled with a great wind and I let out a terrifying battle cry.

A huge clamour arose from the boys who removed their shirts and roared their own awesome cries. Such was the tumult that football teams as far away as the counties of Armagh and Cavan were struck with terror and fled their all-weather pitches in their thousands and hurled themselves into the sea at Bloody Foreland.

The earth began to tremble and a bloody blaze filled my eyes. I sprang at Paddy Roberts and taking him first by the throat I shook him until he was a rattling bag of bones. Once rattled, I flung him thirty yards against the far wall where he hit with a sickening thud and slid like a bag of slack to the concrete – a dead root – unanswerable. A perfect line.

I was on him in an instant and once again I cast him from me – this time against the opposite wall and soon the alley was awash with blood and entrails. The boys were delighted; the staff subdued.

I assumed my full height and gazing up at the battle crows still hovering above me, I yelled:

B! A! L! L! O! C! K! S!

With each hero-yell I hurled Roberts against another bloodsoaked wall. This continued for three days and three nights. Staff and pupils pitched their tents and feasted on fishcakes and mince and huge vats of water were prepared to release me from my warp spasm when the time came. Such time did not arise until the morning of the fourth day when I was duly lowered into the first vat. Such was the fire in my contorted frame that the barrel erupted in huge blasts of steam and exploded in all directions. The second vat boiled over and hissed dry and only in the third vat did I begin to settle and regain my shape.

I was sent to the nurse – a plainclothes nun – who was able to confirm that I had indeed undergone a state of warp spasm and was quite definitely one of the tribe of Danu. As I lay there on her warm leatherette couch I heard the excited cries of my comrades outside. They had placed the head of Paddy Roberts on a pike and were parading lithely around the school. A considerable crowd had gathered to witness their triumphant progress –

Behold the creatur! they shouted, Behold the creatur!

As I listened to their celebrations and sucked on a thermometer I tried for the life of me to recall what had happened. Paddy Roberts was dead and I had killed him in a cruel and unusual way while under the influence of warp spasm. I was confused and a little shaken.

One good boke and you'll be right as rain, reasoned the nurse. You'll not know yourself!

I've never told anyone this before but I never felt so much as a featherweight of guilt over the whole affair. In fact, all I experienced was amusement and smug pleasure. I was well pleased with myself and outside the chanting of the boys tickled me no end! What's more, I knew I would be certain to get away with it.

Don't worry your head, said the nurse. There won't be another word about it in a week's time.

She was right. Once the bishop had been informed, Paddy Roberts was hastily buried under the all-weather pitch and the whole business of the Battle of the Box Alley was completely hushed up. The school, I was told, might not have survived the scandal.

FOUR

According to the catechism I had a soul. It was a bit like my heart but it wasn't exactly there although, if anywhere, it was probably in the middle of my chest. Every time I committed a sin a black mark would appear on my soul and if I sinned all the time my whole soul would go black and rot like a potato. I learned all of this from the nun in the first class.

There were two types of sin. Venial sins were little sins and mortal sins were big sins. If I died with a mortal sin on my soul I would go straight to hell. If I died with a venial sin on my soul I would go to purgatory. If I died with no sins on my soul I would go straight to heaven and see God. That was about it in a nutshell.

There was another type of sin called original sin and you were born with this whether you liked it or not. It was all Adam and Eve's fault and they were our first parents. The only way to get rid of the black mark of original sin was to be baptised. If you died before being baptised you went to limbo which I believe has recently been theologically closed down.

Even in my venial days there was little or no chance of dying without at least some kind of sin on my soul so the chances of heaven were slim. The only way would be an act of contrition at the moment of death or to be struck by either lightning or an automobile upon leaving a confessional in a state of grace.

God gave Moses ten commandments and these were the rules by which we had to live our lives. Luckily, very few of these commandments had any relevance to my life and caused little concern – murder, wives and oxen could safely be ignored. The sixth commandment might as well not have been there at all – apparently damn all to do with either myself or the Sisters of Mercy.

But those were innocent days long before Augustine's clouds of muddy carnal concupiscence gathered over the damp townlands of Fermanagh. The older I got the more sins began to define themselves and stick like goosegrass to the calves of my legs. Sins against the Holy Ghost, Sins against the Church and a plethora of subsections and paragraphs added to God's hitherto exhaustive list. The mysterious commandment number six suddenly swelled from an irrelevance into a serious problem.

Now it meant (apart from adultery) bad thoughts, bad actions, bad looks, bad gestures, bad songs, bad women (Brigitte Bardot), bad movies, bad newspapers, bad poems, bad jokes and bad anything. Inclusive yes but by no means clear – all moral dilemmas were left to fester and congeal in and around the unexplained commandment number six. Bewildered and unsure whether I was in breach or not, there seemed to be no theological oracle who could be consulted.

Hadn't I little to worry about! How insignificant my crimes! How little the evil as compared to what follows! *De minimis non curat lex.* Oh how horrible the sins now corroding my soul! Murder most foul! Best of it all – I didn't care two hoots! Not one continental damn! Next day I was on a boat with a continental dame.

My sins so far are obvious:

Smoking: the breathing in and out of the smoke of tobacco –

pipe, cigar, cigarette, opium, stramonium, gauge, mezz, hash, cane etc. put that in your pipe and smoke it, smoke like a Trojan/chimney/train etc.

I had purchased for my own pleasure Twenty Regal Kingsize and smoked them all in a reckless bout of gluttony in a recumbent position that doubtless amounted to sloth. Thinking myself a great fella altogether I was also guilty of the deadly sin of pride. Also, my inhalation of this carcinogen further amounted to a shameful attack on my own body which is the temple of the Holy Ghost. That so many clergymen smoke is frequently explained away by the commonly held belief in their day that smoking killed germs. Aye surely.

Drinking: to swallow spiritous liquor with a view to its entering one's bloodstream and creating an adjustment of one's mental state; to drink the bit out, to drink to this or that, or drink up, have yous no homes to go to?

I purchased for my own pleasure twelve creamy pints of stout and consumed each one with giddy relish. These were followed as you may remember by tequila slammers. The sins herein are all of the above plus the occasion of sin that excessive drinking creates. Sins of lust, anger and covetousness inevitably ensue and suddenly your neighbour's ox looks worth having. In a state of drunkenness one is a disgrace to oneself, one's family and to the country at large particularly if criminal damage is caused by the almost certain boke into the pocket of a nearby sportsjacket or, worse again, all over a friend's fireball carpet.

Swearing: to use profane oaths to express anger; fuck away off! oh shit! ah ballocks! The sin here is in its expression of anger and in the offence it can give to great-aunts and clergymen.

Against this there is a biblical warning to beware the anger of the righteous man and it is my experience that even the most righteous of men are known to resort to such linguistic taboos – often with hugely satisfying and humorous effects. Packie Bonner appeared to swear in the Italy game.

Murder: the unlawful killing of a human being with malice aforethought; I could murder a pint of stout, to cry blue murder, this is murder on the feet.

I had murdered Paddy Roberts the psychopathic pedagogue at the big boys' school and in doing so had clearly sinned against the fifth commandment and the laws of the land. Perhaps an even greater sin however was my marked lack of regret and indeed the certain pleasure that I felt at seeing his head paraded around the school – Behold the creatur!

Sins of Lust: the many sins contained in the catch-all provisions of commandment number six. The *bateau ivre* incident on the winding banks of Erne was a occasion of such sinning. Again, as above, I have recorded little remorse and indeed would be inclined to encourage what amounted to a very pleasant and liberating experience. This kind of attitude is in itself a sin and has the country the way it is.

Criminal Damage: destruction or damage without lawful excuse of property belonging to another, intending to destroy any such property or being reckless as to whether any such property be destroyed or damaged. I am not entirely sure where this fits into the God/Moses agreement but it is doubtless a sin to boke, as I did, over Joseph Haverty's 'Blind Piper' in the National Gallery of Ireland, Merrion Square West, Dublin 2.

So here we have a series of wrongdoings and sins and might I now suggest that as a little experiment to pass the time, we arrange these sins in the order of their evil. Is murder at the top? Or perhaps swearing at a teacher? Does one consider drinking more heinous than smoking? Does one regard bad language as more deplorable than on-board fornication? Is my callous reaction to Paddy Roberts's death less offensive than the thought of 'The Blind Piper' dripping with boke? These are the questions so far. Mind you, you don't know the half of it.

Caute legendum!

My childhood now in part explained, you will be aware of the two shakes of a lamb's tail perversion from bird-watcher to rake. This all by way of background in order, as Heraclitus said of the Delphic oracle, neither to reveal nor conceal but to indicate. The indications are that I was heading for the precipitous rocks of desire and the whirlpools of vice – and heading there with considerable alacrity and enthusiasm.

This shameless decay was however matched by a rather more wholesome and parallel development. As I have touched upon earlier I had begun to hear the music in the trees – a music heard as I sang and dreamed – as the poet said:

But he heard high up in the air

A piper piping away,

And never was piping so sad,

And never was piping so gay.

When I discovered in such an accidental fashion that I was a descendant of the Tuatha Dé Danaan it was of course clear to me why I was hearing this fairy music. It was the music of my ancestors leaking from the *síthe*. The fairy host was sending me tunes to ease my soul and gently soothe the growing torture in my heart. It was a music I had never heard before and felt sure I would never hear again – that is until one night there was a concert in the technical college. The group was called Planxty and there for the first time I saw a man strap on the elbow pipes. His name was Liam Óg Ó Floinn.

As soon as he began to crann and pop and charm me with those Ennis ghost Ds, I recognised at once the sound of the *sí* – the piper piping away. These were the sounds I had heard in the bullrushes and flags – these were the sounds of the other world.

The concert itself remains with me only as a memory of revelation. Planxty sweated a lot and Liam Óg sported a haircut and sideburns appropriate to the era and looked not unlike a Mancunian professional footballer. One elbow pressured the bag, the other squeezed the bellows, fingers quivered and rolled, the heel of the hand vamped on regulators, a wrist was brought to bear on baritone and tenor keys and he whipped the chanter up off his leg for the bottom D. Complex, intricate, controlled and beautiful and above all this magical activity his face remained impassive and his back straight – a visible nobility and goodness – a hero-light shone about his head. I sat at his feet and wept.

This beatific vision of Liam Óg Ó Floinn was momentous. I purchased for my own pleasure Planxty tapes and devoted myself to the study of the pipes. It would be many years until I would be able to strap on a set for myself but for now I contented myself with ancient manuscripts, cassette tapes, long-playing records and of course the music of the *sí* – notes given to me on showery summer evenings in the Celtic Twilight Zone. It was a music Augustine could never hear.

It's all a catchpenny! he said

That sour remark marked an end to our friendship and my first fracture with the church.

Author's Note

According to Suetonius the pipes were played by the Emperor Nero who was by all accounts a bad egg. But for all his wickedness never let it be said that he couldn't hold a tune. Fiddles my arse! As Rome burned down around him there was our man Nero squeezing away at 'The Bucks of Oranmore'. Would you credit that?

End of Author's Note

FIVE

Mia? Hello? Mia (clears his throat) is that you?
Right boys! run like hell!

And off down the street with us – myself and my two New York companions like three hares and Woody Allen in lukewarm pursuit. We knocked all sorts of doors around Manhattan but Woody's was the best value because of the intercom and that great voice of his. He nearly caught me once and addressed me with a word I had never heard before – somewhere between schmuck and shitehawk.

There was myself, Flaco and Bud. Flaco was from home and had ended up in New York for reasons which will become clear presently. Bud purported to be a New Yorker but his southern drawl occasionally suggested otherwise. Both were in their own ways quite mad and the best of company although given a choice between the two of them, give me Flaco any day of the week.

The Manhattan door-knocking fad was entirely at his instigation – it was a mischievous pastime which he had practised with great skill back home and he claimed to have provoked clergymen from both sides of the community divide to swear with passion and throw missiles with unexpected accuracy. Bud initially condemned this sport as juvenile but nevertheless took to it like a Central Park duck to Central Park water.

Flaco John James Joseph McHugh was born in the townland

of Inisthoin in the county of Fermanagh and little is known of his early years. He attended the same school as myself but as he was one year my junior, our social paths rarely intersected. He was however present among the throng at the Battle of the Box Alley and often spoke with great admiration about how I had conducted myself on that day.

Flaco had acquired his rather unusual name when his father decided to name him after a character in a movie called *The Wagons of Lust*. This was a western showing to packed houses in the picture house in Bundoran in the county of Donegal on Ireland's western seaboard. Mr John James McHugh and Miss Mary Kate Maguire were at the time walking out together and found themselves in the particular Bundoran picture house after a hard day's rain-strolling on Roguey Rock. The young couple were full of love for each other and took great licentious pleasure in the fact that the local parish priest Father Kirwan O'Donnell had decreed *ex cathedra* that *The Wagons of Lust* was a bad film. The offending scene concerned a sweating garlic breathed chavala luring the main character (Flaco) under a wagon for reasons of sexual congress. She said something in Spanish about 'pantalones' and this, Father O'Donnell assured the people of the parish, meant 'bloomers'.

Attending this denounced film was for John James McHugh and Miss Mary Kate Maguire a most liberating and awakening experience. The next day they did not go to Roguey Rock but rather splashed out on a room in the Great Northern Hotel – the end result was a big fat lump of a baby boy and they knew in their hearts that they just had to call him Flaco.

I didn't know much else about him other than that he had written a moderately successful novel about his alleged vampiric tendencies. The book had gone down well with young girls and sensitive boys and Flaco had taken full advantage of his popularity. For a period he had dressed only in black and allowed himself to be seen on the street only after dark. The book was full of sex, violence and a rather sensitively portrayed endless quest for a lost love. All of this along with his odd manner and high cheekbones made him something of a temporary cult.

Popular and all as he was among a certain Saturnian readership he cut no ice at home and was virtually run out of town by a silently disapproving working-class bourgeoisie. The book was a dirty book and he was a quare playboy. He shook the dust from his feet and headed for New York – leaving his cult status behind and taking up a life of bar-room banter, readily available hallucinogens and women who accepted him for the fairly anonymous ordinary Joe he was. He liked to party, he liked people who liked to party and that was about the height of it. He was a real good guy. A swell guy. A decent spud. A trooper.

Dwight Bud Belmondo was a horse of another colour. He was about thirty – a little older than both myself and Flaco – and I met him on my very first night in the city – he was hanging around Port Authority and I have little doubt that he was there for the purpose of robbing new arrivals like me. He claimed to be a native but it all became rather vague when his accent cleared now and again and I tended to place him south of the Mason-Dixon. A conman from the start – a miserable, hard, uptight, twisted piece of wreckage – but the best of entertainment. He bought drink all around him, had a permanent supply of the Devil's Dandruff and attracted the strangest and most exotic of women.

I knew nothing for certain about him. All I knew was that he had spent stretches in various state penitentiaries for several unnamed offences and had passed the time singing in doo-wop groups. My initial interest in him arose during a conversation about a group he had during a spell in a prison somewhere between Rolling Rock, Ohio and Detroit, Michigan. Turned out he was the only person I had ever met who had worked on a chain-gang – although maybe this, like his accent and possibly his name, was a complete fabrication.

Looking back now I suppose I admired him for his capacity for badness. He possessed not an ounce of guilt nor the slightest remnants of belief in any kind of moral structure. For myself (and I think for Flaco in those days) we were getting pleasure from being bad and knowing that we were being bad. Bud was different – he didn't think in terms of good and evil – he thought in terms of himself, his own life and his own pleasure. Bud Belmondo saw himself as part of a chaotic universe and all he had to do was tread water and take plenty of Bolivian Marching Powder – nothing else merited even the slightest consideration.

We stopped in a breathless huddle about three blocks away.

I'd love to have my photie taken with him, gasped Flaco, I think he's the head chief banana! The last time I was inside the Statue of Liberty I was with a woman . . . or . . . sorry . . . the last time I was with a woman I was in the Stat . . . ah balls! Whatever it was he's a droll boy!

As usual we all ended up in a pub and commenced the breeze to shoot and the fat to chew. Pitchers of beer were cheerfully ordered and lavish tributes were paid to Milwaukee.

It's an old Indian word, said Bud, you should in fact say M'waukee. It means the Drinking Place of the Speckled Bear.

Your arse! announced Flaco, it means the Island of Kathleen or the Oak Grove of the Connollys – everybody knows that!

Yeah, sure, Irish wiseguy . . . everybody knows that . . . asshole!

What made Milwaukee famous, grinned Flaco, Jerry Lee

The Killer Lewis! Mad as a cut snake! He's some tulip!

Listen man, said Bud quietly, Johnny Cash is the main man out of that deal.

Do yous know there was a piper called Johnny Cash? I interrupted. He was born in the county of Wexford in 1832 and he was a great man for the horses.

Bud didn't hear me.

You see that Million Dollar Quartet? It weren't worth a dime without Johnny Cash! Don't give me none of that Elvis Presley stuff . . . man I don't want to hear it!

Ballocks! screamed Flaco, wasn't Johnny Cash at the toilets the whole time! Off goes the Man in Black to the bogs without a word to anybody – not so much as a by your leave! For all we know he might be there yet! Stuck in the jacks in Memphis, Mississippi!

Tennessee, asshole!

I bet you can't spell it, you big phoney Yank!

Bud seemed to drift off.

Memphis, Tennessee, he muttered, 706 Union Avenue, Memphis, Tennessee.

Author's Note

The beer goes down rather well and another pitcher is ordered up – then another and I'm quietly confident that there may well have been another. There is furthermore, a very strong chance that several more unaccounted-for pitchers may also have featured in the evening's activities followed by assorted shorts and slugs of lethal distillations from the southern states.

What this means is that much of what I remember is unclear. Some things happened for sure, some things didn't happen for sure and some things happened in the deepest of stupors and

I'm not sure whether they happened for sure or not. I confess that fact and fiction are at times interchangeable within the actual confines of my memory and that this confusion may transmit to others. *Mea culpa, mea culpa, mea maxima culpa. Me a cowboy, Me a cowboy, Me a Mexican cowboy.*
End of Author's Note

You meet the best of people in the jacks, I said in tender reminiscence.

You do indeed, agreed Flaco.

Nothing was said for possibly a whole hour while each of us settled into our own thoughts and preoccupations. How in the hell did we all end up in New York in a bar on West 46th Street in the present company? None of us really had very much in common other than the fact that we all worshipped with great devotion at the altar of Bacchus – we were his senior altar boys and turned out for all ceremonies whether obliged to or not. What brought us together was that we were all lost in the same jungle – Augustine's shadowy jungle of erotic pleasures. Yes we were lost all right but the reason for our situation was simple. We had each walked into this jungle from different directions and spun around so wildly that not only were we lost and disorientated but we didn't even know from which direction we had come. This place in which we found ourselves might well have been another world – a world so different from the one we had left behind that it was impossible to return or even pass once more between the two.

I think the three of us slept. Flaco with his forehead on the bar, Bud with his chin on his chest and me with my head hanging back and my gurgling mouth open like a Marble Arch cave. We would waken up later and talk some more.

SIX

Late one evening there was something of a tumult outside Tommy Makem's Irish Pavilion on 130 East 57th Street. I was on the sidewalk with my two arms in the air and singing away at the top of my lungs – the song in question was a popular ballad known as 'Kelly the Boy from Killane'.

Fling your beavers aloft
And give three ringing cheers for
John Kelly, the Boy from Killane!

A reasonably attentive audience had gathered to clap along, stamp their feet and otherwise offer encouragement and it was evident that they were thoroughly entertained. Among their number however was a pot-bellied middle-aged cop called Captain James T. Martin of the county of Cavan who was less than enthusiastic about my abilities as a singer of ballads and was determined to cease my cantata.

Come on you! he said, placing his half-pound of sausages hand on my shoulder, You again! The Fermanagh man! I'm taking you in!

I protested loudly and attempted to reason with the second-generation Cavan cop.

Get your hands off me ye gobshite! It's a free country! I'm only singing!

You're drunk *again*! he chided. You're a pain in the ass and I'm taking you in for your own good!

I was off again:

> With brave Harvey to lead on the van;
> But the foremost of all in the grim gap of death
> Will be Kelly, the Boy from Killane!

The number of people gathering to witness this piece of street theatre was starting to alarm Captain Martin and he began to drag me way – his two hands under my two oxters.

Bob Dylan's in there! I shouted, pointing in the window of Tommy Makem's Irish Pavilion, and Tommy won't let me in! I only wanted some Chicken Keady! What harm would I have done Uncle Bob? Sure he's only an oul folksinger! I bet you he doesn't know the words of 'Kelly the Boy from Killane'! The same fella! Not a bit of him!

The precinct was by now becoming very familiar to me. It was like a room from somewhere in my childhood – that endless rural idyll spent in front of the television watching *Kojak* – the peculiar ring of the phones, the fat cops with loose ties and stained shirts, the coffee cups and fans and the cage in the corner. I spent a fair bit of time in that cage and was usually released without charge but this time Martin seemed serious.

I was apprehensive. I sat there with my cheek leaning against a bar and avoiding any eye contact with my customary companions – several gum-chewing hookers and a suspiciously tall woman in a red frock. There was also inevitably someone in a surgical mask talking about the Middle East.

Captain Martin was in his fifties. He had a kindly face and a bald head and although he had a belly on him he was a strong, fit man. His father had come from Virginia in the county of Cavan and Martin had inherited something of his wet, guttural lilt. To be perfectly honest I quite liked him – he was in no way dangerous and I suspected that the only reason he pestered me was because he liked talking to a Fermanagh man. He only ever talked about one thing and this is where fate once again interfered in the printworks of my life – Captain Martin was the finest player of the uilleann pipes in the city of New York. Now isn't that a good one?

Up until this particular night however I only had his word for it and I must confess that I doubted him to a considerable extent. It was at precisely the moment that Martin threw a glance at me through the bars of the cage that my life changed. I was convinced by the expression on his face that he was about to book me and when he began to reach under his desk I was sure that my days as a rake were about to end on Riker's Island. Martin produced a large plastic hold-all and, carrying it under his arm, he unlocked the cage door, came in and sat down beside me.

I want to show you something, he said.

He opened the hold-all and began to extract, bit by magical bit, a set of beautiful pipes of ivory, ebony and silver. He looked at me and I looked back at him. We understood the mystery and Martin smiled.

The bag is made from basan, he said, bazil it's called – none of your rubber here! These pipes were made by the great R. L. O'Mealy of the county of Westmeath – made the whole lot! Turned the ivory and cured the skin – just look at that would you! It would break your heart.

I had no words. I just gazed at the pipes. Not since Liam Óg Ó Floinn had played with Planxty in the technical college had I seen a set for real. Martin began to strap them on. My fellow jailbirds seemed strangely uninterested.

Do you know, said Martin, that Lord Edward Fitzgerald himself, the fifth son of the Duke of Leinster, could pipe the birds out of the trees. A gentleman piper! And Sporting Captain William Kelly of the Curragh of Kildare who played for the King of England! He was a great man for the horses and he taught Dan Donnelly to box.

At certain tantalising moments he quivered his fingers or squeezed some silent air through the bellows but each time he relaxed again and began to talk. He told me about Dudley Colclough, Alderman William Phair, Jeremiah Murphy, Piper Gaynor, James Gandsey, the King of the Kerry Pipers, Kearns Fitzpatrick, Patrick Coneely, Soldier O'Farrell, Old Jemmy Byrne, Patrick R. Bohan, the Hogans of Cashel, Martin O'Reilly, the Blind Piper of Galway, John Cash of Wexford, Edward Joyce, Morgan Galwey, Nicolas Burke and Turlough McSweeney, the Donegal Piper.

Ye sons of Apollo come listen to me,
And a comical story I'll tell unto ye
Of a musical janius that came 'cross the sea,
To represent all Irish pipers.

When he came from New York to the great World's Fair,
He met champion Murphy of the auburn hair
And big blowhard Ennis from the County Kildare,
Who call themselves all Irish pipers.

When he got his engagement, late in the spring,
He took his seat with an air that would rival a king.
Some friends went to see him and presents did bring
And called him the Donegal Piper.

He had but one reel called 'Up the Broomstick'
And all other reels he would pitch to Ould Nick;
The way that he played it was but an old trick
For that man called the Donegal Piper.

He played every day from the time he got there
And the Touheys and Flahertys came in for their share.
Such trios as they sure would make a man swear
That e'er heard a genuine piper.

When his flat-throated chanter and pipes gave a squall.
They were like the screech of an owl or a whippoorwill's
                                                    call!
Why, Mozart or Beethoven wasn't in it at all
With this man called the Donegal Piper!

I've heard all the pipers from round Skibbereen,
And from Ballinafad up to sweet College Green;
Arrah! such a mimic on Irish was never yet seen
As this man called the Donegal Piper.

But now he is gone and our spirits are low,
And I say God be with him, *go deo's go deo.*
Since Ireland was scourged by that villain Strongbow
You never have heard such a piper.

Search Ireland all o'er from seashore to seashore,
From the cliffs of Cape Clear to the rath of Gweedore,
And you'll ne'er meet a man such a musical bore
As the one called the Donegal Piper.

Captain Martin clearly had tears in his eyes and in an effort to disguise his sensitivity he reared up in front of the very tall woman in the red frock and hit him or her a clout round the ear. The hookers just muttered 'asshole'. Philistineheads!

Captain Martin, I said, that was beautiful and I thank you for your tales of the gentlemen pipers and the blind pipers of Kerry and the Hogans of Cashel. I thank you too for showing me your ancient set of R. L. O' Mealy pipes and I ask you with the greatest respect would you not consider playing a tune upon them?

And why would I want to play for you, you drunken scut?

Well, Captain Martin, it's just that you have the pipes strapped on and your fingers are hovering over the holes and your elbow is poised upon the bag. I thought it would be grand to hear 'The Virginia Reel'.

At that Captain Martin smiled and said that he would play some day when the humour was on him. He tested me on my knowledge of the pipes and, clearly surprised, he questioned me further about where I heard the music. I told him of my devotion to Liam Óg Ó Floinn and how I often purchased for my own pleasure cassette tapes and old 78s. He seemed pleased by this but when I told him that I could also hear the music in the sally bushes, in the bullrushes, in the whins and in the very wind itself, his face froze and he seemed unable to speak. He stood up and stepped away, gazing at me with the widest of eyes.

You have heard, he stammered, the music in the wind and in the sally bushes and in the whins? You have heard this? Do you know what you have heard?

I do indeed, I told him, it is the music of the *sí*. It is fairy music.

And do you know what you are yourself, he asked, his expression growing wilder.

I do indeed. I am of the Tuatha Dé Danaan – the ancient people of Ireland.

Well boys a dear! he gasped.

Captain Martin sat down again and went into a deep meditation. He rubbed his eyes and his forehead and his temples. He cracked his knuckles and stretched his arms – all the time sighing and gasping and smiling and saying boys a dear. Finally he turned to me and asked very nervously –

Tell me, have you ever heard the sound of the *sí* . . . in New York?

Many's the time I have, I replied. Many's an evening I sit on a low mound behind a rhododendron bush in Central Park and I hear the sweetest of music – tunes like I have never heard before – all of it played on the sweetest of pipes.

Do you be drunk when you hear this? he asked.

Indeed and I do, I said.

He took me once again by the elbow and escorted me out through the cluttered desks of the precinct. It wasn't far to Central Park so he lead on with great dynamism along the busy late-night streets. The air was alive with the warm electric glow of shopfronts and the smell of pretzels and dogs. Martin wore his cap far back on his head and I couldn't help feeling that I was in a movie of my own making. When we got as far as Central Park Captain Martin turned and said:

Show me!

I walked into the park and Martin nipped along lightly behind me. We didn't have far to go because the rhododendron bush in question is at the Plaza Hotel end.

Here it is, I said, pointing at the bush.

Right, said Martin, sit down. The two of us sat on a low mound and Martin gazed into the bush. It was a beautiful warm, balmy summer's night and I could have murdered a bottle of wine. Instead Captain Martin quizzed me about the Tuatha Dé Danaan and the music that I had heard from the *sí*. I denied nothing and told him all I knew − on one condition − that he would teach me to play the pipes. He agreed and we remained there until dawn waiting and waiting for some sign from the *sí*. Nothing happened. We waited the whole of the night but not so much as a single half-note. Disappointed and with the sun rising over the city, myself and the New York cop went for coffee in a noisy place on East 60th.

I suppose, whispered Martin with obvious sadness, you're the only one can hear this music and you'll only hear it when they decide to give it to you .

Yes, I agreed, you've hit the nail on the head.

Author's Note

A poet of middling status is wearing a scarlet waistcoat as he walks into the bar of a fairly tasteless Belfast hotel. Upon immediate inspection it is obvious that he is vain, arrogant and deeply in love with his own image of himself. He is accompanied by a carefully dishevelled student type who is clearly pleased to be in the company of the poet.

The two approach the bar and the politeness of the barman indicates recognition of his literary customer. He attempts cheerful conversation:

If you don't mind me saying so, sir, I greatly enjoyed your collection.

The poet turns to his tousled companion and declares:

Quite incredible! Even barmen are reading my poems!

The ragged-trousered acolyte grins and runs his hands through his hair.

Mmmmmhh, he agrees.

The poet orders two pints of lager and suggests that the barmen transport them to the table by the window. The barman nods:

Certainly sir.

For the rest of the evening the scarlet-coated poet and his incoherent disciple swallow pints of lager and smoke cigarettes of their own design. The poet talks of death and peacocks. His companion listens and breathes deeply.

Little do they know that they are drinking slops. Little do they know that they will drink slops everywhere they go. Little do they know that every barman in the world will feel the need to serve them slops. That is all they will ever deserve. Little do they know.

End of Author's Note

Flaco was first to waken up.

Right boys! What's the difference between Abraham Lincoln and Bill Clinton?

I give up, I said, rubbing my eyes.

Do you give up, Bud? shouted Flaco, digging Bud in the ribs.

Ah, go away, man!

Do you give up?

Do I give up what? moaned Bud.

What's the difference between Abraham Lincoln and Bill Clinton?

How the hell should I know?

Flaco was delighted with himself.

Only two of them have beards! Get it? Only two of them have beards!

Bud was not amused.

Jerk!

When the penny dropped, I laughed my leg off.

By this stage the bar was empty and had assumed the condition we liked best. All around were stacked chairs on tables and soft stools with the tracks of peoples' backsides in them being dragged across the floor. Barmen were washing glasses and asking us whether or not we had homes to go to. We were collectively as full as one hundred and twenty badgers and had, truth be told, no serious thoughts of home – real or imagined. We were comfortably numb and would be hard to shift.

It was customary at this hour of the evening when the bar exuded a certain deserted romanticism for each of us to say a few words. It was, I suppose, an effort to relocate and work things out and take advantage of our mental realignment to say things we might not say in another place at another time.

Speech! shouted Flaco.

Ah, no, man! groaned Bud.

Come on! Bud first!

Bud did not stand up but simply gazed at his glass, by now swinging precariously between forefinger and thumb. He closed his eyes tightly and exhaled –

All I want to say is this. Somewhere along the line I guess I got into bad company and things started to go a little wrong. It was all the narcotics I guess . . . all the heavy shit I was doing back then. I stopped writing to my mama. I guess I had nothing to write home about. Then there was this girl on the scene. She was a real lady . . . but then she split. Ah what the hell! Here's to the Confederacy!

We had heard this speech a million times and never really expected to hear anything else.

Is it true, asked Flaco, that you shot a man in Reno just to watch him die?

Bud finished off his glass in two gulps.

Yeah, he said.

Flaco stood up and banged the table with the butt of his glass.

Hello, I'm Flaco John James Joseph McHugh and I'm a total mess. I am the Wreck of the Hesperus! Anyway! This squirrel goes into a bar and drinks all night long. At the end of the night the squirrel is very, very drunk and the barman advises him to go home. The squirrel staggers off but returns again about five minutes later and starts scraping around under the seats. What's wrong with you? asks the barman. The squirrel looks up at the barman and says, Have you seen my keys? I'm locked out of my tree!

What?

I'm locked out of my tree!

Ah, make the damn speech! shouted Bud angrily

Right you are, nods Flaco gathering himself, Reverend fathers, Reverend mothers, Ladies and Gentlemen! Boys and Girls! I'm Flaco and I'm a complete balls. I miss the lough and I miss the hills and I miss Cuilcaigh mountain. I miss the cubs and cutties and I miss the Lucozade lights on the Cornagrade road on a wet winter's night. Apart from that I'm as happy as the day's long!

What I'd really like to say is that I thank God for good company and good drink and I thank God for Jerry Lee Lewis and Johnny Cash and what a swell party this is! At half three the Mount Lourdes girls come gushing out the gates in their purple and their turquoise and there's big yellow school buses and . . . ah fuckit!

With that Flaco fell backwards and missing his seat entirely, landed on the flat of his back on the floor. He lay there in the spilt drink and broken glass and laughed a pathetic silent laugh. Me next.

In this state of advanced drunkenness I was feeling particularly expressive and with that came a conviction as regards my own coherence. I remained seated, Bud put his head on the table to regard me sideways and Flaco continued in the prone position.

What I want to say gentlemen is this . . . and I know I'm half tight and I'm slabberin' but what I want to say is this. You see the great musician who was a drunk man? Oh yes! He was a great musician and had been given all the tunes in the world. He might have got them from God or he might have got them from the fairies – wherever he got them from he had a gift. Oh yes it was a gift all right! No other bloody way to explain the way he could coax a lament from the *Dudelsack*. He was a gifted man but he drank like a fish and let himself down. He was undependable, he was lazy, he was excessive, he was bad-tempered and he treated women so, so badly. Now I'm not making excuses for him but he was gifted.

Ah, not this oul routine again, said Flaco, still with his eyes shut, here we go Charlie Parker!

You see Charlie Parker? I went on with great *gravitas*, you see Elvis Presley? You see Little Willie John and the late great Johnny Ace? All of these people were gifted – they had been given something; they were supermen! What they had was beyond other men – it was supernatural!

Jerk! blurted Bud, who seemed on the point of nausea.

47

Now let me explain, I said, smoothing the air out before me. Who do we know who was a superman? Jesus, right? He was beyond other men and yet he was a man – he was a superman. And what I'm saying is this. The great piper and Charlie Parker and Little Willie John and Johnny Ace and Elvis Presley were all like Jesus in reverse – kind of in negative.

Know what I'm saying? They were men but they weren't ordinary men – they were supermen and beyond other men. They could do things other men could never do, they had gifts other men could never have and in a way they became all of our potentials.

Jesus was all our positive potentials and these other guys – John Coltrane was another one – were so nearly all of our positive potentials that in the end they became all of our negative potentials. They were all of us at our limits – of strength and of talent but also of weakness.

Jesus had superstrength; these men had superweakness – but no less men for it. They had been given all of our talent and all of our weakness and they just couldn't carry. They were superhumans – people at people's absolute limits.

I mean, what happens? The great piper falls drunk over his pipes every night of the week and the music leaves him for dead. Johnny Ace buys a '55 Oldsmobile and shoots himself in the head with a .32 in a game of Russian roulette. Charlie Parker playing God's music and poisoning himself with dope.

Yeah, yeah, shouted Bud, Jesus in reverse; we've all heard this before!

Yeah but listen, I'm serious about this, Elvis Presley loved his mama and . . .

Who in hell's blazes, chirped Flaco, is Long John Willie?

His name was Little Willie John and he could sing like an

angel. He killed a man who wouldn't let a lady sit down. He died in jail.

I put my head on the table and announced that the whole lot of us were now living on the flip-side. A cop was called in off the street and we were escorted out. We had no homes to go to.

SEVEN

*D*o *you really believe all of that?*
　　All of what?

All of that reversed Jesus stuff? Man at his limits?

Indeed and I do. Who are you when you're at home?

I am your conscience. I am the thing that used to tell what was right and wrong.

Were you informed?

Indeed and I was.

I don't hear too much from you these days so I don't.

Indeed and you don't. I do my very best, mind you! You just don't listen.

Ah yes I hear you now and again but I choose judiciously to ignore you. You were becoming a problem.

Do you believe all that stuff you were saying?

Indeed and I do.

You can't go around making up your own theology!

Why the hell not?

Mind your language!

Sorry.

I'll tell you why. Better men than you thought it all up and you'd be very vain to think yourself better than them. The sin of pride is a terrible thing. It's deadly.

So I'm supposed to swallow everything?

Indeed and you are.

And what would you know?

I'm telling you – I'm informed! I'm not the light of nature itself but I am the eye which measures and takes it in. I am your practical judgement.

But you could be totally wrong?

I cannot be wrong. I am not a false conscience; I am a right conscience and a right conscience must be followed at all times.

What if you are invincibly erroneous?

Follow me!

I don't buy this at all. Go pick on someone else!

What if I told you I was a doubtful conscience?

Then I'd examine you. Go away!

Look at you! You're as full as forty badgers and you're a mess! Your companions are less than ideal and things will only go from bad to worse. One of them wrote a dirty book. The other one shot a man in Reno just to watch him die. All your heroes are hard-living, hard-drinking, pill-guzzling, dope-shooting freaks, and you try to turn it into something else!

Yes and I'm right to do so. Wasn't John the Baptist as mad as a cut snake?

I've never met the gentleman.

Well take it from me.

Come on! You're a waster!

[It had me in a half-nelson.]

I am not a waster. I am finding myself. Look at St Augustine. You gave him a long leash?

He was a one-off and you don't even come close. Don't ever try to justify what you're doing – all that 'make me chaste but not yet' bullshit!

Mind your language!

I apologise. Look you're breaking every rule in the book, and don't tell me you don't know it! And by the way, your behaviour towards women is deplorable!

[It had me in a full-nelson.]

What happened to you? You were put on the right road from the start! You have no excuse!

Ah I just strayed.

Ballocks! Don't give me the stray from the path line! You took a decision!

OK then, smartarse! When did I take this famous decision? When was it exactly? Where did I go wrong if you're so smart? Was it the woman in the men's toilets? Was it the warp spasm business?

Did that really happen?

Of course it happened. Were you not there?

I think it is a conscienceless state. Right enough there are three or four days during your adolescence which I simply cannot account for.

That would be it then.

Fair dues.

But you can't answer me, can you? You cannot tell me where I went wrong?

Don't give me all this pretence. You don't give a damn about any of these questions! You're just trying to make yourself more interesting!

[A leg-press!]

A Lisnaskea leglock!

Look I don't want to have this conversation! Why do you show up like this just when I'm in a good mood? Just whenever I'm happy out you come out of the woodwork! Why do you do that, eh?

I am your conscience. It's my job.

I suppose somebody's got to do it.

Are you going to sort yourself out or not? Are you going to remove yourself from these occasions of sin or are you going to hurtle on through chaos and deny all you know to be true?

I don't know anything.

Yes you damn well do! Catch yourself on! Get a grip!

Ah, take yourself off will you!

I knew my conscience was right. My conscience always seemed to be right. These days however I had developed the ability to ignore it and carry on in a cold and callous way. When my conscience came to wrastle I would wait for the very moment of submission and simply step out of the ring.

Author's Note

The phone rings several times and finally I decide to answer it. It is Frank Devine – an old schoolfriend who came out of the theological closet and decided upon a life in the spiritual cloisters of some odd order of St Somebody in the county of Clare. Such is the divergence in our respective paths that their ever intersecting again is an absolute impossibility. He is, however, a pal of old and a welcome voice.

Hello there boy! says he. How's she cuttin'?

Ah Frank, says I, it's yourself!

He has just finished his evening prayer and meditation and is sitting upright in his neatly furnished room provided for him by the order of whatever saint it is. A black wooden crucifix and an alarm clock stand side by side on a locker. An anorak hangs over a chair and the lemon quilt has been sent by his aunt. Outside, cherry blossoms blizzard to the breeze and Frank is at a loose end.

Are you keeping well? he asks.

I am. Are you?

Grand, says he.

I am drinking from an exceptionally large glass – Charles Heidsieck Brut Reserve of Reims, France. I am pouring the remains of the bottle into the glass of my languid companion who is stretched to her full glorious length along my antique *chaise longue*. She is eating freshly picked, still-wet strawberries in a most erotic fashion and I am distracted by the manner of their consumption and cannot concentrate on what my diaconate friend is telling me down the phone all the way from the county of Clare.

Are your folks well and all the brothers and sisters? asks Frank.

The very best, says I.

And yourself? You're in good health?

Ah you know yourself, Frank – it's all champagne and roses!

Of course, says Frank, and sure why not?

My beautiful companion leans her head back and smiles. I tell Frank that I'll ring him back at the start of next week.

End of Author's Note

EIGHT

N ow this tune that I am about to play is called 'The Snowy
Breasted Pearl' and it was often played by the great Leo
Rowsome of Ballintore in the county of Wexford. I heard him
play this very tune in Carnegie Hall and it would have brought
a tear to a stone!

With that Captain Martin of the New York Police Department began to play and the sweetness of his tone and the
precision of his harmonies were beyond compare. All was going
at once – drones and regulators – fingers, wrists and elbows. It
was an all-consuming and magical sound and I was filled with
such sadness and longing that I began to weep real tears.

Not for the first time, Captain Martin had ordered me to
meet him by that particular rhododendron bush in Central Park
where I had heard the music of the *sí*. I had agreed to meet
him on this occasion only if he would bring his pipes and
commence the promised lessons. It was quite dark and the park
was deserted and the notes of Captain Martin's O'Mealy pipes
ascended to the silver clouds of a new-moon sky. The fairy
folk, I was sure, would be listening.

Captain Martin demonstrated various stylistic techniques
from the crann to the pop. He explained the difficulties of
overblowing to reach the upper octave without affecting the
deep dronetone of the drones and he expressed enthusiasm for
the free employment of grace notes.

The average ear might not even hear them, he said chirpily, but I'm a terrible man for the grace notes. I play them fast and I play them faster – decorative notes they are – decorative notes before the note or in the middle of the note or maybe even after the note. Grace notes, my boy, are the very secret! *Appoggiatura!*

You mean, I offered, a note above the principal note interpolated before it and momentarily taking its place in the rhythm of the passage?

That's it exactly!

As the night grew darker and colder Captain Martin played on, his eyes shut and every limb overcome by the music of the soul: 'The Top of the Cork Road', 'Castle Kelly', 'The Frieze Britches', 'The Boys of the Lough', 'The Banks of the Suir', 'May Day', 'The Cuckoo's Nest', 'Kiss the Maid Behind the Barrel', 'Touch Me If You Dare', 'The Flogging Reel', 'The First House in Connaught', 'The Copperplate', 'The Blackbird' and 'The Lark in the Morning' – nearly every tune in the world. Myself and Captain Martin were both entranced but finally my impatience got the better of me.

Captain Martin, I said, you are under a *geis*. You have promised me that you will teach me the playing of the union pipes and it is my fervent desire that such educational matters commence immediately. It is not that for one moment I am fed up listening to your cranns and pops and grace notes but it is nevertheless a fact that I grow weary and impatient and I feel that the time has now come for me to strap on bellows and bag!

Indeed and it has, said Captain Martin gravely.

The pipes were unstrapped and carefully passed to me. It was like being handed a baby. They were delicate and yet strong and had life in them. They were more special than I was and the expression of awe on my face would have communicated such to the casual observer. With silent solemnity I buckled buckles and slid my arm into the leather strap of the bellows. The regulators and drones lay across my legs and the bag nestled under my oxter. I took the exquisite ebony chanter in my fingers and began to tease out a noise.

It was at once a sweet noise – a long unending low note that might have lasted forever but for what happened next. A great wind rose up around the rhododendron bush and Captain Martin fell back on his elbow and covered his eyes with his hand. A huge swirl of dust and leaves hurled itself towards us and an insect-jewelled shaft of light shone from the bush.

God save us! shouted Captain Martin.

A faint music grew louder and it was the sweetest music I had ever heard. Captain Martin could hear it too –

God save us! he shouted again, it's the fairy music!

Hup!

Squinting towards the bush I saw only whirling leaves and bright light and then as I looked down at my fingers I saw that they themselves were moving, no less! The music grew louder and I saw that it was me who was producing this music the likes of which would never be again. I was afraid and yet ecstatic and I began to laugh, holler and gulder. Captain Martin was almost hysterical with delight –

God save us! You're playing the pipes! Fair play to you!

The music got faster and faster and the tunes kept coming one after another. Neither myself nor Captain Martin knew the names of any of them and we can only assume that they were all fairy tunes. When these given tunes suddenly stopped we realised that it was dawn and that I must have been playing for hours. My fingers were frozen and could move no more, and I slumped over the pipes. Looking towards the rhodo-dendron bush I saw the whirl of leaves and dust begin to subside and it was then that I saw the most beautiful woman I had ever seen. She was tall and slender and her face was the colour of apple blossom. Her golden hair fell in ringlets about her shoulders and a band of gold curved about her brow. Her eyes were as green as gemstones and her lips as red as blood. The robe she wore was of the finest silk and was embroidered with the most delicate of silver thread.

Is mise Niamh, she said, I am Niamh. *Je m'appelle Niamh*.

Of the Golden Hair? I asked.

There is no proper word for yes in the old tongue. Yes. *Oui*.

I think I love you, I blurted.

Cinnte. Oui bien sûr. Very likely.

What happened?

Na píopaí? The pipes? *La cornemuse?*

Yes.

Na Daoine Beaga. The Fairies. *Les Fées*.

Will I always have these tunes?

There is no word for no in the old tongue. No. *Non*.

Why not oh Niamh of the Golden Hair? I am of the Tuatha Dé Danaan and I love you more than my own life.

Mar is deargréice thú! You're a drunken hallion! *Vous êtes un chèvre!*

But do you love me, itself?

B'fhéidir. Perhaps. *C'est possible*.

As quickly as she had appeared she disappeared again, leaving me in the deepest of shock and in bad need of a shot of the Wild Turkey. Captain Martin who knew more about all of this than he had let on told me that sometimes the fairies would give the music to someone special but only for a brief period.

They had to be thoroughly worthy of the gift in order to receive it in full. He reckoned that Niamh of the Golden Hair was indeed probably in love with me and had offered me the gift of the music for a short period in the hope that I would reform, give up my ways and be worthy both of the music and of Niamh herself.

As Captain Martin packed away his pipes I thought of Niamh of the Golden Hair and the great beauty of her brow. That she might love me was more than any Fermanagh man might ever desire but then, as I reminded myself, I was of the Tuatha Dé Danaan, the Tribe of Danu, the ancient people of Ireland, and I could hold a tune like nobody's business. What was a poor boy to do?

I walked back to the precinct with Captain Martin and he told me that I would never be able to play another tune until I had won the heart of Niamh of the Golden Hair and merited a place among the good people. I promised him and myself that I would prove worthy. I sat down at Captain Martin's desk and he was called away. When he came back he had a face on him like a Lurgan spade.

I'm afraid it's bad news kid, he sighed, it's your pal McHugh – what's his first name, Flaco? Yeah well anyway, he's been stabbed. He's dead.

I looked at Captain Martin and I could tell there was more to it.

We've arrested someone, he said.

Who? I asked him, searching for an answer I suspected I already knew.

One Dwight Bud Belmondo. He's admitted it – stabbed the poor guy at least thirty times.

Captain Martin put his hand on my arm.

NINE

Leaving New York felt like one of life's first great defeats. After Flaco's death I no longer had the stomach for the very thing that first excited me about the place. For my period in that city I was in my own movie – it was a place that lived up to every anticipation and fantasy. The look and smell and sound and feel was just as I had expected – the bagels and pretzels, the yellow cabs and steam. This was a city of the imagination that just happened to be real. To give it up seemed at times incomprehensible and to leave it on these terms made me feel cowardly, cheap and half-baked. This was no Bonaparte's Retreat or Dunkirk – no amount of garnish could make this hightail palatable. In my own eyes I was a loser.

It's not that Flaco and I were close but I liked him. To like anybody when your life is one of cynical self-seeking makes that person special. He was a link to something – much like the picture of Liam Óg Ó Floinn that I left hanging over the bed. For all of Flaco's behaviour and the infamous dirty book there was something about him that made him less offensive than the rest of us. He enjoyed his mischief. That bastard Belmondo felt nothing but his own pleasure and nothing either side of it. He had killed Flaco in a row about Johnny Cash! Flaco had said that he could sing none.

For all my feelings about the murder of my friend I confess that thoughts of him bleeding to death on the sidewalk were not my only preoccupation. I had returned night after night to the rhododendron bush in Central Park and waited for the music of the *sí* and the sight of my beloved Niamh of the Golden Hair. Neither Niamh nor music came to me. Captain Martin told me that my affair with the good people was over and it appeared that he had once again hit the very nail on the head.

The image of Niamh of the Golden Hair tormented me in my sleep and many a night I woke up not knowing whether it really had been her or not. Was I receiving visitations from the other world or was I dreaming in a drunken slumber. At times I began to doubt if I had ever seen her at all. I began to wonder about me piping away in Central Park – was that all some kind of vision? A hallucination? So much seemed so real and so much seemed so long ago – dreams confused with drunkenness – fact confused with fiction. I kept asking Captain Martin to retell the story and his recollection was always full and faithful but I was, by now, deranged, unsure and fearful for my own sanity. In this condition, New York was no place to be.

Author's Note

In a pub in Greenwich Village – between St Mark's Place and Alphabet City – a young man in a cap sits with his companions. One is a famous Irish actor who has just completed a performance in The Booth Theatre. He is the toast of Broadway and the world and his wife knows his name. The other companion is a quiet lad from home who is trying to do well for himself in the arts world of SoHo. The three are collectively as full as one hundred and seventy-five badgers and the talk is of home. They drink the health of Donegal beaches, Fermanagh islands and Belfast poison. They laugh and eventually sing 'I'll Tell My Ma'.

The waitress is also from home – somewhere in the county of Down.

What do you do? she asks the famous actor.

I am a mortuary technician, he says.

What do you do? she asks the quiet lad.

I too am a mortuary technician, he replies.

And what do you do? she asks the young man in the cap.

I too, he says, am a mortuary technician.

The waitress looks at the three of them and says,

Yous are not wise.

End of Author's Note

TEN

I was lying on the flat of my back on the cold floor of the Sistine Chapel, Vatican City, Rome, Italy. This was during an unfortunate episode which lasted at least a year and took place in and around several major European cities. Because of all that had happened I felt that I could not yet go home – I feared that the normality would be unbearable and I also knew that I was far from acceptable as a suitor to Niamh of the Golden Hair.

Anyway, there I was on the flat of my back on the cold floor of the Sistine Chapel and all I can say is that I had drink taken. I can only assume that the assumption of this unorthodox position was for reasons of personal security and, I vouchsafe, in order to view to greater effect the works of Michelangelo.

All around me, upright tourists were wheeling about and were, I thought, in an advanced state of peril as regards damnable cricks in the neck. I was convinced that I was in, by far, the more sensible position both as regards an appreciation of the ceiling and, perhaps more importantly, the preservation of my neck. I have always endeavoured at all times never to inflict any unnecessary twists to any part of myself and in particular the delicate organs such as the ankle or the neck. I tell you this by way of information.

Follow me and my pen now and I'll take you on a little tour of the Sistine Chapel. Please remain silent and refrain from using flash photography. Right, ladies and gentlemen, we have just left the Stanza Incendio and now as we descend these steps we enter the famous Chapel of Sixtus – built for Sixtus IV in 1481. This huge wee chapel is the official chapel of the Pope and is also the setting for any conclave of cardinals whenever the time comes to raise the white smoke. I must apologise for any obstruction to your view but this restoration work is being paid for by a Japanese television company. The current debate is of britches. As you would be able to see on a clear day, there is much nudity here in the Pope's chapel. Pius IV wanted the whole lot whitewashed and it took one Daniele da Volterra (a pupil of Michelangelo) to talk him into allowing him to confer some decency on the naked by painting trousers on them. We believe that the Vatican is currently, you'll be glad to hear, in the process of once more removing the bags. Please follow me upstairs now to the Appartamento Borgia!

[Aside] On second thoughts, you go on without me – I'll just lie here on the flat of my back and take a look about me.

The frescoes represent the life of Moses and the Old Testament on the one side and the life of Jesus and the New Testament on the other. In 1508, Michelangelo was commiss-ioned by Julius II. He began work in May and twenty-three years later he was only getting around to starting the Last Judgement. That's a long time in any man's book and it's not a bit wonder the Pope was crabbed. Michelangelo was slow, thran and had a set of bottom teeth that would put you in mind of Charlton Heston.

In my mentally tampered-with state on the flat of my back on the cold floor I began to ponder in a serious fashion much about the human condition and our relationship with the universe. The Separation of Light from Darkness, the Creation of the Sun and the Moon, the Separation of the Earth from the Waters, the Creation of Man, the Creation of Eve, the Fall of Man, the Sacrifice of Noah, the Deluge and the Drunkenness of Noah.

I took each theme in turn and, inspired by the muscley men and women of Michelangelo, I contemplated each to the point of comprehension. I was overcome with religious fervour and believed I had found a purpose. Far from my thoughts were the bars of New York, the handball alleys of Fermanagh and the sweet sound of the *sí*. Even the images of Niamh of the Golden Hair (but not of Liam Óg Ó Floinn) seemed to fade in this place. I was solemn, content and silent – watched over by the Cumaean, Delphic and Persian Sybils. For added company: Jonah, Daniel, Isaiah, Zacharias, Joel, Ezekiel, Molaise and Jeremiah.

With great conviction I began to regard the Last Judgement. There was Christ the Judge with his right hand raised in absolute condemnation – Go ye accursed! His mother was to the right along with prophets and martyrs and apostles. Below on the left was the Resurrection of the Dead – angels, trumpets, the Book of Judgement, the dead coming from an open tomb and entering the Valley of Jehosaphat. I was as full as a bingo bus and quite overcome.

I promised myself major restoration and renovation, an abandonment of my reckless Lothario ways and a return to belief in a morally structured world full of goodness – all of it presided over by the supreme being we know as God.

My meditations were suddenly interrupted when I discovered that two hands had been slipped under my oxters and I opened my eyes to find myself being hauled to my feet by two multicoloured and annoyingly handsome Swiss guards who were wearing tights and carrying pikes. The tourists scattered and looked at me in horror – convinced in their sudden belief that I was the kind of man would attack the *Pietà* (or for that matter His Holiness) with a clawhammer. Little did they know that I had been on the verge of a spiritual breakthrough and could have done well without such a coarse and unwarranted interruption.

I was dragged headlong through corridor after corridor as the works of Raphael, Perugino, Lupari and Giulio Romano flashed by.

Take me to the Pope! I shouted. I am one of the young people of Ireland and he loves me!

The Swiss guards said nothing and simply dragged me ever quicker past frightened files of tourists clinging the walls.

Take me to Redsocks! I shouted.

Everything became suddenly bright and I found myself out on the street – hurled through a Vatican side-door and dumped *ex cathedra*, bell book and candle, out on my ear. Roman citizens sidestepped and shimmied and a huge carved door was closed into the wall.

I sat with my chin on my knees, allowing the bitterness to seep in and fancying I could hear the sound of Nero squeezing away like a loon. Eventually I headed for an Irish bar on the Via San Martino ai Monti and drank like a fish – barred for life from the Holy Sea. In the Hotel Giolli Roma on the Via Nazionale I watched Dana hugging the Pope somewhere in America. All kinds of everything remind me of you. *Irlande douze points. Si prega di liberare la camera entro le ore 12. La direzione non e responsabile per oggetti di valore lasciati in camera. Totus tuus, Urbe at Orbe. Orare, studere, agere. Quo Vadis? Roberto Baggio. The Black Pearl of Inchicore.*

ELEVEN

D ream sequence. 11.00 hr. Les Deux Magots. 6 Place St-Germain-des-Prés. 75006 Paris. France. Tel. 45 48 55 25.

A pot of *café-crème* costs me twenty francs (Pot de 20cl.) and a *croissant au buerre* runs me another ten. It's supposed to be the best coffee in the city and I am in great need of it. I was out the night before in an American bar at the bottom of St-Denis and I have a wooden head. I am to meet my friend Flaco John James Joseph McHugh; he is on the pig's back and loaded with money and this expensive café is his notion of a cheap joke. The café is beautiful, the colour of wheat.

The humorous twist, not lost on my good friend Flaco, is that we should have our rendezvous at the self-styled *café littéraire* – Hemingway, Prévert, Sartre and all them other gobshites. The café a few doors down – the Café Flore – is where Camus tried to score with Simone de Beauvoir and where I, only a week previous, tried with rather more success to tackle Chantal Lafayette – the daughter of a rich man from Sierra Leone. Across the road, the Brasserie Lipp – so far from a Newry chippy.

I sit and wait – not feeling altogether well – not at myself as such. The whole style are strolling on St-Germain. I begin to wonder how I got here.

Bir Hakeim, Dupleix, La Motte-Picquet Grenelle, Ségur,

Duroc, Vaneau . . .

Wrong!

What?

You changed at La Motte-Piquet Grenelle and took the line for Gare D'Austerlitz and got off at Sèvres Babylone.

Indeed and I did not!

Indeed and you did!

Indeed and I didn't!

What?

I took Nation right through Bir Hakeim, Dupleix, La Motte-Picquet Grenelle, Cambronne, Sèvres Lecourbe, Pasteur and then walked for miles around Montparnasse Bienvenue . . .

Yes! Yes! That's the very man! Montparnasse Bienvenue! And then you took the line for Porte de Clignancourt, through St-Placide, St-Sulpice and then, by dad, St-Germain-des-Prés!

You have it! You have it! You've hit the nail on the head there! Mind you I may well have got out at Odéon and walked.

Ah, sure as long as you have your health.

Anyway, there I am thinking thoughts and passing the time at the *café littéraire*. Haven't I little to do!

We'll hardly know ourselves in a week or two.

Suddenly there is a commotion on the boulevard and an agitated crowd gathers on the sidewalk. I sip my expensive coffee and pay the tumult considerable attention. Next thing I hear the sound of horses' hooves and the sight that meets my eyes is the most bizarre yet encountered by either the two of them on their travels.

Coming down Boulevard St-Germain, at great speed, are four black horses running abreast and pulling a large black *calèche*. The driver is cracking his whip like a demon and his wide drawers cover the whole of the box seat. The driver is

Flaco John James Joseph McHugh.

The horses clatter to a stop and Flaco leaps down before me. He is wearing very strange and Gothic gear and the population of Paris seems, for once, alarmed.

Ye boy ye! he shouts, ye boy ye! Yeho ye boy ye! How are you my friend? What do you think eh?

He gestures towards himself and towards his horsedrawn carriage. I think nothing simple.

Don't move! he says excitedly. We must talk!

The good citizens of Paris organise a conveyor belt of sugar cubes direct from the tables of Les Deux Magots straight to the horses' mouths. I light a Gauloise and inhale deeply.

Relax man! says Flaco.

I can see he is up to some class of mischief – as if those bloody black horses weren't enough. He holds out his hand in a stay-put gesture, walks back over to the carriage and strokes the head of the nearest horse, murmuring repeatedly,

What's the long face for?

Stepping up to the side of the carriage he grandly opens the door onto a dark interior. There is movement and slowly a large man of about six foot with a heavy red beard steps out into the sunlight. I don't know him from Adam. He mutters something to Flaco in a very soft Dublin brogue and I immediately place him in Clontarf – scene of the rout of the Vikings and the death of Brian Boru while at his prayers. Flaco is actually leering and the man looks uncomfortable. Flaco leads him to the table.

May I present Mr Abraham Stoker!

Good grief! I'd say you are gobsmacked!

Indeed and I am. I am in Paris with Bram bloody Stoker and a friend of mine who has earlier bled to death on a New

69

York sidewalk! Mr Stoker sits down and Flaco orders more coffee. He asks for le Café des Deux Magots (pot de 20 cl.) I sit and grin as best I can. This is distinctly odd and Mr Stoker clearly finds it rather long-winded.

A huge rumpus to my right and I fear that a fight has broken out. The cause of the confusion is, however, a horde of demented cameramen swelling up out of nowhere and we are blinded by a million flashes going off in all directions.

I believe, says Mr Stoker, that you have undergone heroic warp spasm?

Indeed and I have, I say.

I am very happy for you, he mutters.

Mr Stoker is beginning to appear mildly belligerent.

If you don't mind me saying so sir, I offer, I greatly enjoyed your book.

Which one? he fires back.

I thought you only wrote the one!

He's very fond of *Dracula*, says Flaco, trying to redeem me. We're all very fond of *Dracula*!

Yes, Mr McHugh, I have glanced at your publication – your vampiric saga. It is a load of shite!

Flaco seems disturbed by this and excuses himself by stating a desire to attend to his toilet.

I am left alone with Mr Stoker and the photographers.

I believe, he says, that you are dedicated to the pursuit of pleasure? I believe that you have so far lived the life of the philanderer and the decadent? Would you consider yourself evil?

Well, Mr Stoker, says I, that's a hard one so it is. I have in my time been a bad egg and I believe I have committed every transgression and sin under the sun with several extremely perverted exceptions. I believe that I have been and still am in the sheugh of immorality.

Mr Stoker fingered his beard –

Just one little *t* and you have immortality.

Oh, very bloody clever!

You are familiar with my man Dracula? Do you think him evil?

Indeed and I do!

Well, he continued, he is consummate evil and I know that he would have made a formidable solicitor. I came up with him after too generous a helping of dressed crab and his character was there before me.

Although he is indeed a bad egg, Mr Stoker, says I, I kind of like him all the same. He has it rough. He is unhappy and condemned to an eternal life of misery and lovelessness. He is an outcast from life's feast. He is a painful case altogether.

Flaco returns from the WC and says:

As the other buck Frankenstein's monster said . . . what was it? . . . Misery has made me sad – make me happy and I shall again be virtuous. What that it? Something in that general ballpark.

Mr Stoker puts his hand in his pocket and produces a carefully wrapped package. I open it to reveal a cassette tape. It is a Planxty tape called *The Woman I Loved So Well*.

I awake in L'Église St-Germain-des-Prés. I sit there for half an hour. Blank.

TWELVE

I prowled Paris for a period. Living in an attic in Passy may sound very well-to-do but the reality is that it was a very small, cramped room belonging to a student who was at home with her parents in Les Sables d'Olonne. I wasn't even supposed to be there. I was what you might call a class of a squatter. I lived reasonably – the source of my money is at this stage unimportant although I'm sure it has crossed your mind that this kind of global gallivanting does not come cheap.

I usually ate Greek. What seemed like hundreds of Greek islands had collided behind St-Michel and the air vibrated to the sound of the *bouzouki* and guitar. Windows full of sad-eyed fish, dripping skewered lamb and pigs on spits – *Menu*: 90F. Seafood salad – crab, mussels and tuna. I'd smother it in lemon juice and mop it up with bread and call for wine and the waiter would *Oui, Monsieur!*

I'd tip him and he'd know me for again. Memories like elephants. Brochette Paysanne – chunks of half-cooked, blood-red lamb, tomato, potato, onion, olives, rice and lettuce. I'd call for more wine and the waiter would *Oui, Monsieur!* I'd chuck some bread to the pigeons and maybe they would know me again – see them later on the steps of the Opéra or at Châtelet and they might perch upon my head – memories like waiters.

Le Poseidon, La Vieille Athènes, Restaurant Santorin, Neptune – every day at noon – *Menu: 80F. Oui, Monsieur! Bon appétit*! I'd watch the dizzy tourists who had just come wheeling in off St-Michel. They'd just done Notre Dame and were still pious as bedamned.

I would sit there as happy as Larry in touristville, avoiding the real thing and writing the odd postcard that I would never post:

I'm in the Latin Quarter eating fish!

I'm in Harry's Bar wearing Richelieu's hat.

I'm on Pont-Neuf. It's four in the morning. I hear accordions.

I'm in Conways. The lights are flashing on St-Denis.

It's raining on my balcony. Satori in Paris.

So there was me eating like a lord in Paris – harassed by winos and pigeons and lost Americans and writing posey half-haiku postcards to people at home in their bars and their bedrooms. This was Paris where I was young and nothing was simple. In earnest I would tip the waiters and wander along the Seine or go underground and take a chance: emerge on some beautiful boulevard and sit, drink wine and search the sky for darkness.

You're off your trolley!

Indeed and I am not!

Indeed and you are! Setting yourself up in a garret in Passy? Are we to swallow this? You're a damned liar, so you are!

Do you want to know why I was in Paris? I'll tell you. After Rome I went up Italia's leg to some wee place along the coast near Pisa. One night I was on the beach and the bonfire was lit and we were all eating grilled fish and drinking barrels of wine. The girls were all in swimming and their white dresses were hanging barbed on the bushes – man dear it was a beautiful evening and I was full as fifteen camels. I decided that I would take the train to Pisa for the sole purpose of fixing the damn thing and what do you think happened? Muggins here falls asleep on the train in the company of three French nuns who are too timid to waken me up. I end up in Paris the following morning. Don't laugh – it could happen to a bishop!

Arrah G'way wit'ye!

It was fate brought me to Paris.

Fate of our fathers.

Musha, you have it!

And of this garret?

I was indeed in a genuine real live garret in Passy – a very fashionable part of town – apart from its garrets. Just down the stone steps from the Métro and through a huge oak door and across a cool marble courtyard and into an antique elevator and by that route to my garret. One tiny room – a table, a sofa which became a bed, a coffee maker, a sink, a mirror and, glory of glories, a window! A full length window which opened onto the smallest of balconies and oh what a view! The Eiffel Tower perfectly framed – just one block of houses between me and the river – a bend in the Seine and the Pont d'Iéna. To stand on the balcony with the train-track below, the river to the right and the tower in front, to breathe the burning rubber air of the city, the grey slate, the wrought iron, the flaking shutters, the conversations from the rooms across – mahogany tables arranged for a meal – candlesticks! Oh it was grand!

Grand!

And at night the tower would flicker on – gold against the twilight – becoming an awesome machine, a spaceship's thousand lights, too many to contemplate, the whole structure swaying, looming, alien in a darkening sky. I would toast it every night: *Vive la France!*

You're full of shit!

There was enough to keep me going in Paris. There was enough to keep my mind off Flaco being dead and all that had happened. There was even enough to keep my mind from straying towards the *sí* and Niamh of the Golden Hair.

Aye! She's trouble! Ingrid Bergman!

There I was full of coffee and wine and brie and *pain au chocolat* and perhaps a too generous helping of dressed crab. There I was with my perfect view of the Eiffel Tower. Balzac used to live around the corner at Rue Raynouard – number 47 – a serious man for the women. A hill of beans.

'He was still producing with feverish haste one masterpiece after another, slashing his excited brain with champagne, ether and drugs of all sorts. Women after women in endless succession hastened the destruction.'

What in hell's blazes is that?

That, you idiot, is Axel Munthe talking about de Maupassant in *The Story of San Michele.*

Your oul head! Do you know they called him Le Taureau Triste?

I do.

And do you now what Taureau *means?*

I do!

What?

Bull!

Yes! and that's what it is! Bull! Bullshit! and Bullshite!

And do you know what *triste* means?

I do!

What?

Sad!

Yes! sad! and that's what this is! Sad!

[Aside]
    And he repelled – a short tale to make –
    Fell into a sadness, then into a fast,
    Thence into a watch, thence into a weakness,
    Thence into a lightness, and, by this declension,
    Into the madness wherein now he raves,
    And all we mourn for.

Do you know, young man, that Maupassant died in Passy?
What did he die of?
He died of a Tuesday.
Come on what did he die of?
Syphilis! That's what! Young man, you need to get yourself some rather more attractive role models – less of the Charlie Parkers and more of the St Augustines.
I used to know the man well!
Ah, but you don't bother with him now, do you? Bloody Henry Miller!
Roger Milla!
King of the road!
No! I'm talking about the Roonies!
Roger Rooney? Rooney's path?
The Cameroonies!
Orooni!
Frankie Miller.
Darling!
Honeybun!
Windy Miller! Cider-drinking puppet!
Listen, I have a perfectly good role model in the great piper

Liam Óg Ó Floinn. He is a noble, dignified and honourable player of the union pipes and many's a time I wish that I could play like him. Many's the time I wish the people of the *sí* would once more give me every tune in the world so that I could play like the great man himself. Make me happy and I shall again be virtuous.

You'd be better off saying your prayers!

In Paris I can stay underground forever and never come up for air. Leap turnstiles, risk fines, take the breeze of a roaring train – before and after. In the evenings I imagine I hear the sound of the pipes and I follow it through the maze. *Passage Interdit!* It is forbidden to forbid and I think of the tunnels of the *síthe* and Niamh of the Golden Hair. In Paris, I can take the danger, the beauty, the darkness and the love; everything is in Paris.

Orpheus in the Underwear!

Here there is no need for excuse. I spend the mornings in bed watching the lift go up and down the tower. I get up around eleven and listen to the coffee spitting on the machine. I go off to the INNO and buy a baguette and some brie and I take it all at my leisure on my little *balcon* – the radio tuned to Oui FM.

I go out in the sun wearing my black suit, white shirt and no tie of any description. I cut a dash in my well-polished shoes. I walk along the river to the tower, crossing at the Pont d'Iéna and being drawn under the stance of the tower itself and on up to L'École Militaire. Stop for more coffee at La Terrasse and then the Métro to Cluny. From there I can go anywhere but usually it's into La Huchette to the Pâtisserie du Sud-Tunisien for a sandwich or some colourful, sickening pastry. Perhaps even, and this may surprise you, the church of Saint Séverin – its shadows and arches and chattering birds swooping from window to window above the altar. I sit in a Van Gogh chair and watch. Think about life.

You do in your arse!

Boys but you're bitter!

What about all the creeping and late sleeping? What about all the booze drinking and women fondling? What about all the sin? The crimes of Paris? Tell them about that seeing as you're so bloody talkative!

I walk around gallery, museum, café and market – all too bewildering; too much for only the five senses – the rai and the reggae. The tenor in Montmartre singing ragged bits of *La Bohème*, the Senegalese orator in front of the Pompidou, the fire-eaters, the man with the paper trousers, Rue des Beaux-Arts. Number Thirteen – and everyone in the whole damn place alive and in love.

Ah, shut your fuckin' mouth!

All right, give me a chance and I'll tell you about the crimes of Paris. It is a fact that crimes were committed, that things were done and that I was personally responsible. Me a cowboy, Me a cowboy, Me a Mexican cowboy. As in the past, these sins may fall into various categories according to their seriousness. The order of evil I shall again leave entirely up to yourself. And so, where to begin.

Get on with it, ye slabber, ye!

Right, I fell into bad company in a bar called the Punt Club near the Place des Innocents. There was a CRS van parked permanently at the front door – the rifles arranged like golf clubs in a shop window and those gentle gentlemen of the CRS would think nothing of hurling the odd canister of CS gas into the place at intervals throughout the week. It was a rough spot and the clientele would have been described by my mother as 'a rum crowd'.

The bar was badly lit, all sort of black and cherry red, and just about everybody in there seemed to be hiding from something that was after them. None of this bothered me in the slightest because by the time I staggered into the Punt Club of a weekday night I was usually as full as thirty-seven flamingos.

I met a woman there called Lara. I didn't like to admit it to myself at the time but I found myself going there every night for the simple reason that I wanted to see her. She was beautiful, grey-eyed and tall. I knew very little else about her other than she was from somewhere near Reims and her surname was Heidsieck. That didn't seem French to me but Lara was full of contradictions. She spoke very crisp, almost public-school English, she was a devotee of French football and often spoke lovingly of Michel Platini and Dominique Rocheteau. She drank like a fish, was a professional thief and was, I can say without fear of contradiction, the sexiest woman on earth.

The night it became clear that she wanted me to kiss her I was consumed by a weird and wonderful feeling – Oooh Aaah Wonderbra!

I would like you to kiss me, she breathed.

Would you indeed? says I trying to be cool.

Yes, she said, yes.

Oh, very funny and quite inevitable!

When I finally stopped talking and starting kissing I found my mouth open onto the great warm universe. My right leg began to shake and my tipped brogue made a noise like a turkey pecking a wooden floor. I kissed her to the point of lockjaw and then she led me by the hand through the shiny wet streets of Paris.

Her apartment was large and well-furnished – somewhere

off Alésia in the Fourteenth. Everything in it was soft, comfortable and fragrant. I knew I would be happy here –

I'd like you to stay, she said.

Would you indeed?

Yes, she said, yes.

OK! We got it the first time!

I stayed. In the morning I was very unwell and I boked on the peach tiles of her bathroom.

I have revealed several details about Lara Heidsieck which cannot be simply glossed over. The fascination for association football may be of rather less interest to you than her profession – a rare and ancient trade. It is hard to credit but it is true that she was indeed a professional thief. There was a room off to the left and it was coming down with the paintings, vases and jewellery a go-go. There were six indentical Picasso prints – all signed by Pablo himself. There were shoeboxes overflowing with pearl necklaces and there was a suitcase full to the lip with watches, bracelets and rings. I am no expert in any of this but I was intrigued to notice fine examples of Tyrone Crystal deep in the horde – a twelve-inch Killybrackey vase which I believe retails for one hundred and thirty-five pounds. There were also fine examples of Devenish eggs which go for around nineteen pounds and ninety-five pence each – not to mention a tall Fintona candlestick, a Donaghadee nine-inch footed bowl worth about one hundred and fifteen pounds and fifty pence and two Ardree brandy balloons – seventy-eight pounds the pair.

That's a fair whack so it is!

Where did you get all of this stuff? I asked.

I nationalised it, she said; sleight of hand, burglary, art theft. As you might say yourself, lover, it was wee buns!

I stayed in Lara's apartment for about three months. We had good times together but I'm afraid I must now look back on that period with regret and shame. Already in this reminiscence I have committed many foul deeds but it was that first encounter with Lara Heidsieck which led to the gruesome crimes of Paris.

Right, smartarse! Tell them how you lived!

She stole. I ate.

That is disgusting! You are the limit so you are!

I'm afraid it's true. I lived like a lord in Paris because Lara would come back every evening, have a shower and then meet with her connections in the Punt Club. I would join her later and we'd both get blocked on Ricard, Cognac and Kir Royal. I asked no questions and she had no hang-ups; it was, at the time, the perfect relationship.

And what happened to your beloved Niamh of the Golden Hair?

I tried not to think about her.

And what about Liam Óg Ó Floinn? And your precious pipes?

Look, it wasn't easy, any of this!

You're a gobshite!

Maybe so. Anyway I lived like this for about three months. I was not in love with Lara because, deep down, I was afraid of her. Her simple approach to decadent living was matched by a simple and callous approach to everything else. She always carried a knife and once again I never thought it appropriate to ask questions.

Go on! Tell them about your little offence against commandment number seven!

It was late one evening and I was in and around Montparnasse just killing time. I got completely plastered in the Dome or somewhere like that and when I came out I took a wrong turn. I was walking down a dark street which was probably parallel to where I had just been and I suddenly heard the sound of the pipes. This had been my first encounter with the music of the *sí* in a very long time.

I thought I was imagining it at first but as I leaned my ear to the air I could definitely hear the sound not of one but of many pipes. I thought I had come upon a very large *sí* perhaps with a thousand fairies and I was both excited and afraid. I thought of Niamh of the Golden Hair and that night in Central Park. Was it the host calling me once more?

I walked further along the street and stopped outside a huge olive green door. There was a door within the door and I entered slowly. As I emerged into a courtyard, the sound of the pipes grew louder – many pipes all playing at once. I followed the sound into one of the buildings and stealthily pursued the swelling noise up a flight of stairs and along a corridor. The music was beautiful – like no sound I had ever heard before. Never had I heard so many pipes play in unison; there must have been hundreds of bellows being elbowed and hundred of bags being squeezed. I stopped at another door and I knew they were within. I gently edged it open just enough to see inside and there I saw the most peculiar and wonderful sight – forty badgers were playing away to their hearts' content! The tune is one I will always remember and I could lilt it for you at the drop of a hat. Suddenly the badgers turned towards me and laughed forty mocking fairy laughs.

I pulled back from the door and when I looked back again they were gone.

I entered the room looking for some trace of what I believed I had seen: the fairy host appearing to me in the form of beasts of the wood. I had often heard of their ability to do this but this was indeed the first time I had experienced such pistrix at first hand. The badgers were gone but just as I turned to leave I noticed that they had left something for me: lying on the hardwood floor was the most beautiful set of union pipes you have ever seen. They fair gleamed in the lightbulb light and I was overcome with fear. These were fairy pipes and it would be bad cess to anyone who would touch them.

I was however as drunk as a skunk and I did have this unnatural perverted perversion and obsessional obsession with the pipes. It was, I'm sure you'll agree, highly unlikely that I would leave them lying there to be manhandled by the concierge or any other man in off the street. These pipes had been left for me – they were a gift of the good people – and I would take them home. I carefully lifted them off the floor and cradled them in my arms. At last I had pipes of my own.

Balls! You stole them! You were drunk out of your head and you wandered into the Pipers Club on Rue whatever it is and you stole somebody's pipes. Admit it! You're a tealeaf!

Ah, what do I know?

What did you do with them?

I got scared on the way back to Lara's appartment. These might have been evil fairies and they might have cast a spell on me if I kept the pipes. I sat down on a bench in that wee park across the road from Notre Dame and I had just started to strap them on when a terrible fear came over me. They might not have been the good people at all. I would be cursed if I played these pipes and I might be turned into a pig. Quickly I released myself from them and ran headlong across the road and flung them as far as I could into the Seine. When they hit the water I heard a scream. It sounded porcine to me.

Having admitted that you were living off immoral earnings

*and that you stole a set of pipes and, of course, that you were living
in sin with someone who very definitely amounts to a bad woman,
would you care to tell us about the first grand boke?*

Since you ask, I will tell you. As you will recall, this tale
begins with a boke of tremendous proportions and significance.
Its significance has not yet become apparent but from here on
in all will become clear. There have of course been other minor
or secondary bokes such as those which occurred after my on-
board encounter with the German tourist and following a long
night with Lara Heidsieck. These bokes were due entirely to
the mixing of drinks and should not be confused with the much
more significant boke about to be outlined.

I had never been up the Eiffel Tower and I decided one
fine hungover morning that it was time I had ascended the
city's premier landmark. I boarded the lift with many other
people – among them citizens of Japan, the United States of
America and several of the Scandinavian lands. The lift swung
and jolted and people screamed and giggled. I cursed them as
tourists and remained calm. As Paris grew smaller below me I
marvelled at the achievement of man.

When we reached the top I separated from the tourist flock
and walked with determination towards the edge of the tower.
It was a clear day and I looked first for my old garret in Passy
and with the aid of a telescope provided for the purpose, I
could see right in the window. There was somebody else living
there now – a fat bald man who looked a bit like Paddy Roberts
– if you can remember him. (Behold the creatur!)

I picked out all the sights – Sacré-Coeur, Saint Sulpice, the
Pompidou, the Arc – and I breathed the thinning air. Paris had
assumed its beautiful colour of golden blue and I was for a
moment, content.

You were like a pig in shite!

That is not the sort of vulgar expression I would use myself but I suppose I was indeed like what you say. Anyway, I was atop this fine structure – its four legs curving inwards and rocketing its latticed self up into the Paris skies.

It weighs 7,000 tonnes, you know.

Begorrah, you're bang on!

More substance, my boy!

Right, so I'm up the Eiffel Tower and hanging over the edge and looking about me. I am perfectly relaxed and suddenly I get this monumental dig in the ribs. I twist myself around to see who it is who has attacked me in this way and I discover that there is nobody there. Despite the pain in my ribs I recommence my survey of the city. A moment later another dig, this time more vicious. Once again there is nobody there. I am confused and nauseous with the force of the blows to my abdomen and it suddenly dawns on me that somewhere in the back of my throat there is a welling boke. It is too late and in a matter of a split second a fearful spray of boke is free-falling the nine hundred and eighty-four feet to earth.

(There is some scientific opinion that might suggest that all might have evaporated within seconds but there is a more primitive school that would be concerned for the citizens of Paris below.)

Did you form any opinion there and then as to what might have been the meaning of all this?

I admit that I did consider it odd to receive two blows from an invisible attacker – two blows that led to the unfortunate boke. I admit that there appeared an unnatural hand in this episode. I thought at once of the badger-fairies but I was of course very wrong – but that is all for later.

So just to recap: you lived with this professional thief, the highly-sexed Lara. You lived well because you spent all of her money. You stole a set of pipes and disposed of them by chucking them into the Seine, and to top it all you threw up all over the edge of the Eiffel Tower. You are one sick puppy!

It gets worse.

Tell us a joke.

A man says to his wife that he always loved horses but he was too fat to be a jockey.

His wife says, 'You are too fat to be a horse!'

Boys, but that's a good one! I must remember that!

THIRTEEN

When I finally made it back to Ireland I was no more certain of where ought I to be than ever I was. Why I made a beeline for the county of Clare I'm not a hundred per cent sure but I would say that it is a safe bet that I felt the need to meet immediately with my old friend Frank. You will recall that much earlier Frank, who was at the time studying to become a priest, called up out of the blue. I was unable to concentrate on what my dear friend was saying because I was at the time in the company of a beautiful and languid companion who sipped champagne and sucked strawberries. I told Frank that I would ring him back in a week but of course I didn't and the week was spent in stretchy sleep and lovemaking of a most pleasant nature.

Frank was surprised to see me:

Well, what a surprise! I thought you were away off around the world visiting the great spiritual centres!

Aye surely, Frank, can I come in?

You are very welcome. Give me your coat and I'll make us a nice pot of tea.

Tea! That'll harden you!

Frank was ordained by now and had a great air of content-ment about him. He wore an old fashioned soutane and it had the effect of blocking him out from the neck down. Everything seemed irrelevant apart from his head and the occasional glimpse of his socks as he whisked by. He was red-faced, hefty and well-fed.

How's the religion business? I asked.

Oh very good, lots of customers you know.

We drank the tea and talked about nothing in particular for quite a while. I was annoyed at the completely uninteresting house in which he lived. There seemed to be none of him in it – no books or records or pictures or anything. All seemed regulation issue and I wondered how he could be happy.

Do you like it here? I asked.

It's grand, Frank said.

Do you know what it is? I blurted eventually. I'm way off the main road! I'm lost Frank. I don't know whether I'm coming or going!

Frank put out his hand.

Steady on there! What's wrong with you? Leave school with A-Level guilt did you?

Come on Frank, you know I left before then. All that Paddy Roberts business. You were there yourself!

You bet I was! Didn't I hold your coat?

Yes; well, I went away after that and things have gone from bad to worse. Yes I had a great time but it's been all wrong! You name it Frank I've done it! I want to be virtuous again Frank! But they're after me! The bad fairies! They're on my tail!

Did you ever learn the pipes? asked Frank with great concern.

Ah Frank! don't talk to me!

We looked at each other and Frank could see that I was in a bad way.

What do you want? he asked kindly.

Frank I want to be good! I said. How do I be good?

Well, you cannot hope to be good without the help of God's grace and grace is obtained chiefly by prayer and the sacraments. Saint Paul said that without faith it is impossible to believe in God. You do believe in God don't you?

Ah Frank I don't know what I believe in!

Well, we'll see. Faith isn't enough anyway. There must be good works as well. You must do good works.

What kind of good works? Tell me! I'll do them!

Without God you can do nothing, whispered Frank with great solemnity. You also need the grace of God. There is a supernatural element to be dealt with here. Let me explain. The supernatural order is made of two things − a supernatural end and the means of attaining it. The supernatural end is the beatific vision of God in Heaven and the only way to attain this end is through grace.

Frank, this is very long-winded! Just get to the point and tell me what grace is.

Frank stood up and placed the cup and saucer on the mantelpiece.

It is the essential condition of our union with God. It is a supernatural and freely-given gift of God. It is given to us for our own salvation and sanctification. It restores Adam's loss. Have you ever stolen anything?

No.

Anyway, continued Frank, when God the Son became a man and died for our salvation he restored to us the gifts which Adam had lost and purchased for us the right to grace and everlasting glory.

Ah Frank, this is hard to believe! This is all out of a book! You probably don't believe it yourself!

Frank was calm.

I believe it with my whole heart, with my whole soul and with my whole mind. If you want to be good you must be in a state of grace. External and internal grace. You're getting some of the former now just by listening to me! The internal graces are bestowed quietly on your soul: Faith, Hope, Charity, inspiration and good thoughts. Do you ever have good thoughts?

I have nothing but profoundly good thoughts about Liam Óg Ó Floinn, I said.

That's good, nodded Frank, that's good. You see, although graces are gratuitously bestowed it is the all the same Spirit. St Paul was on the case there! As he said in his first letter to the Corinthians . . .

Are you sure we want to hear this?

G'way!

. . . to one indeed, by the Spirit, is given the word of wisdom; and to another the word of knowledge, according to the same spirit; to another faith; to another the grace of healing; to another the working of miracles; to another prophecy; to another the discerning of spirits, to another diverse kinds of tongues; to another interpretation of speeches. But all these things one and the same spirit worketh, dividing to everyone according as He will.

I bet you're sorry you came!

God renders the soul pleasing in his sight by acting upon it and permanently abiding within it. I am talking now of Actual Grace, Habitual Grace or Sanctifying Grace. Actual grace is the work of the Holy Spirit on the soul and it is a passing supernatural aid which will help us to defeat evil. It enlightens your soul and helps to overcome temptation. You're going to need a lot of actual grace if you hope to get out of whatever sinful hole you are in. You cannot arise out of your sin, nor can the good man persevere in virtue without bucketloads of actual grace! Fortified by grace, you can resist all evil!

But Frank, I said, I'm not getting any of it!

Frank once again had an answer:

Even the most evil sinner receives graces. The trick is that he must listen and react. As I live, saith the Lord God, I desire not the death of the wicked, but that the wicked turn from his ways and live.

And who said that? I asked.

Ezekiel, announced Frank on the minute.

Right enough, I agreed. So what you're saying is this, grace is a supernatural gift freely given by God and which the Holy Spirit freely communicates to our souls. It makes us all children of God, pleasing in His sight and heirs to the kingdom of heaven. In other words it cleanses the soul and makes it beautiful and holy in the sight of God. It makes us temples of the Holy Spirit, sons of God and heirs to his kingdom.

That would be about the height of it in a nutshell, smiled Frank.

We had more tea and I was was very conscious that I could have murdered a stiff one. There was no drink in the house and this seemed like neither the time nor the place. I continued my quest for theological knowledge by questioning Frank about life, death and the universe in reverse order. I found that we could agree on very little. His concepts of existence were limited to reality and the Bible and he had no experience whatever of, for instance, the Land of the Fairy Host, Paris or New York. He had been to Rome and had spent some time examining the walls and ceiling of the Sistine Chapel although he had done so in an upright and sober position.

I asked him about the Devil.

Is the Devil for real? I asked.

As real as you and me, he counselled.

But you don't believe in fairies and pipe-playing badgers?
No.

You don't believe that I am of the Tuatha Dé Danaan?
No.

You don't believe that I heard the music of the *sí* coming from a rhododendron bush in Central Park and was indeed given every tune in the world by the good people themselves?
No.

You don't believe that I am in love with Niamh of the Golden Hair and that one day I will be worthy to be with her in her own world?
No.

And yet you saw me with your own eyes go into heroic warp spasm and pulverise the Wombat?

I saw what I saw and I believe.

Ah but you also believe in the Devil! Does he have horns or what?

He does not have horns of any description.

And I suppose you've seen him, have you?

I have – and I see him now. He is in you my friend. The Devil is in you.

There you are now! What did I tell you!

I finished my tea and launched a vicious attack on the clergy and on the institutionalised religion. I told Frank that he wouldn't know temptation if it came up and licked him on the ear.

I suggested that Frank was talking firstly through his hat

and later through his arse. I lost all sense of decorum and began to rave and swear like the craziest of loons. I was talking as if I believed in nothing. It was clear that I had not kept the faith. Frank politely asked me to leave and when that failed he threatened me with the leg of a chair.

I'll put your shaggin' lights out, you son of Satan!

I left faithless and friendless. Welcome back to the Land of Saints and Scholars.

On the head of all this Devil business I was well shook. I had heard Jerry Lee Lewis expound upon this subject and it certainly put the wind up me. The penny suddenly seemed to drop that all this evil and sinning which was going on may have had some relation to the thing we call the Devil. This realisation moved things into another dimension.

My meeting with Frank was not a success. I am unsure as to what I had hoped to achieve but one thing was clear. Just as I had been physically dumped out of Vatican City I had now been spiritually and emotionally dumped out of the house of goodness. I was without question out in the dark – lost among the whirlpools of vice and the precipitous rocks of desire

I decided to learn more about the new world in which I had blindly come to live.

FOURTEEN

began to study the various occult philosophies – purely for reasons of self discovery, I might add.

O my prophetic soul!

I was very interested in a man called Agrippa.

Ah! So now were getting down to it! A bloody oul sorcerer!

DE OCCULTA PHILOSOPHIA

Ah, you're the quare fella! That Agrippa one was the Archimagus himself! Didn't he have a schwarzen Pudel?

A what?

A big black dog like Caesar Curry.

So did Velvetcollar.

And who is Velvetcollar when he's at home?

The Devil. My grandfather's uncle James saw him slipping through the rushes with a big black dog.

This is all getting out of hand now. Be very careful, my lad!

I am particularly taken by the concept of inspired melancholy so I am. I believe I am Saturnian.

You're a ballocks!

Spell it!

To hell with you!

HYMNUS IN NOCTEM.

Hymnus in Cynthiam! O dear God! Cynthia Ní Mhurchú. The Eurovision song contest! Niamh of the golden hair! Man but you're gettin a bit out of hand! Moonlit visions, my arse!

Come consecrate with me to sacred Night

Your whole endeavours, and detest the light . . .

That's enough of that oul! I'll get the priest for you!

No pen can anything eternal write,

that is not steept in humour of the night.

You bloody mad eejit, you! I suppose you're reading Chapman and Dee?

And Pico della Mirandola!

Oh, Sacred Heart! I implore you to desist and cease these studies. Get back to the pipes! Think about the noble countenance of Liam Óg Ó Floinn! You should read De la Demonomanie des Sorciers *– or* Dr Faustus*! Look what happened to him!*

Get up the yard!

And it has indeed come to our ears that boys like you and indeed girls with a similar approach to life are abandoning themselves to devils, incubi and succubi.

Who said that?

Pope Innocent VIII. Papal bull, 1484.

And who wrote *De La Demonomanie des Sorciers* if you're so smart?

Jean Bodin, Paris, 1580.

You have an answer for everything don't you!

Indeed and I do.

Do you know that when you mix heroic frenzy with melancholic temperament you get great men?

Like yourself, I suppose?

I wouldn't like to say.

'Il Penseroso'! Where I may oft out-watch the Bear.

Milton.

Fluid.

Glaser.

Starsky and Hutch
The ultimate poetic expression of inspired melancholy.
If St Augustine could hear you now!
He wouldn't give me the time of day!

Author's Note

When John Hammond organised the From Spirituals to Swing concert, there was one man on the bill who did not perform. The story is that Robert Johnson died at the very moment he was told that he was booked to play at Carnegie Hall. He looked at the handbill and saw his name.

The New Masses Presents:
An Evening of American Negro Music
From Spirituals to Swing
(Dedicated to Bessie Smith)
Conceived and Produced by
John Hammond.
Directed by
Charles Friedman

Robert Johnson was born in Hazelhurst, Mississippi and he took to playing the guitar in and around Robinsonville and beyond. His travels took him as far as Canada but he spent most of his time on the dirt-tracks and floodplains of the Mississippi Delta. Robinsonville was a great place altogether for the corn whiskey and Robert drank like a fish and played at jukes all over.

The thing about Robert Johnson is this. Like Signor Niccolo Paganini before him, the story is that Robert Johnson sold his soul to the Devil. I've spoken to Louisiana Red and he won't play his tunes on the head of it. Talk to Honeyboy Edwards: he knows what's what.

Robert Johnson couldn't play a note to save his life and then all of a sudden he could play like nobody's business. How do you account for the like of that? All the old musicians say but the one thing. Robert Johnson went down to the crossroads, to the fork in the road and waited, guitar in hand. It was twelve o'clock midnight and along comes a tall dark man with a big black dog. The man takes Robert's guitar and tunes it for him. When he hands it back Robert is his. The bargain has been struck with the Devil himself. Robert can play and sing and the Devil has his soul. Fair exchange is no robbery.

Some do not believe that Robert Johnson sold his soul to the Devil but none can tell why it was that he could play the way he did. None can tell how he could walk from town to town through the worst of dustbowls and never a stain on his suit. None can tell where he lived. None can tell how he died.

Some say that Robert Johnson died on his hands and knees barking like a dog. They say he was poisoned by a woman who put something in his whiskey or killed by a jealous husband. Others say that the Devil came back to reclaim what was his by right of the bargain and that's some conundrum. On the death certificate, the cause of death is given simply as *No Doctor.*

And Robert Johnson sang:

> I went down to the crossroad
> fell down on my knees

I believe it. This is more than just a primitive attempt to explain a gift. If Robert Johnson believed he had sold his soul to the Devil – then he had. Oh yes I believe it all right! The Devil is real person. He is there. Robert Johnson met him at the crossroads:

> And I said 'Hello Satan,
> I believe it's time for us to go.'

I'm talking about Robert Johnson and there's only a couple of photographs and twenty or so recordings left. In one of the photographs Robert is wearing a black pinstripe suit and is holding a guitar. I have a suit the very same. Someday I will wear it in a photograph so I too can cut a dash on someone's bedside table, sideboard or cluttered mantelpiece. It is a grand suit in the best of double-breasted, shiny, undertaker black, never soiled no matter what haystack, dustbowl, dirt-track, railroad, juke-joint, chickenshack or one-horse town. No stains, no tears, no crease. A clean suit was part of the picture and part of the deal.

The last girl who had a photograph of me on a bedside, table, sideboard or cluttered mantelpiece called him a Devil Boy. The first time I saw her scared was when she heard him singing 'Hellhound on My Trail'. I'd bought it in a sale and cheap at half the price. I told her all about Robert Johnson and how he sold his soul for what he had to be. Then she was afraid of me.

End of Author's Note

I don't like the sound of this one little bit!

FIFTEEN

You've only heard the half of it. I was in a public house in Dublin City, Ireland and I had just executed one of my spectacular bokes. It was the usual affair and followed the customary pattern. A punch in the ribs and then another and then the outpouring itself. The public house in question was in Baggot Street and I decorated its floor with eight half-digested pints of porter much to the horror of its regulars, among them a tasteless journalist who reported the event in detail in the following morning's paper.

Such was the drama of my bokes that I became quite well known around the city and the unexpected projectile boke made an unwelcome appearance at all sorts of venues – poetry readings, ballets, dumbshows, the RDS Horseshow, the Imagining Ireland Conference, a Finbar Wright concert, an All-Ireland Final etc etc. – the list goes on *ad nauseam* so to speak.

I was very concerned at the frequency of these bokes and it must be said that they were not solely confined to occasions of excessive drunkenness. Indeed it is the case that their occurrence seemed entirely arbitrary and at the whim of some unseen force. I was most uneasy.

I boked over politicians, broadcasters, officers of An Garda Síochána, journalists, bastard media people from hell, rock stars and representatives of Comhaltas Ceoltóirí Éireann.

No boke was ever deliberate but such allegations were hard to refute. My notoriety spread and my entrance to a public place was greeted with a sudden silence and the shuffle of feet as people sidled off into the distance leaving me in a pool of my own space. It was never easy to make friends.

Late one evening in a Dame Street bar I was approached by a jumped-up poet and his disciple. Such was the vanity of the poet and such was the posturing of his friend that I feared a perfectly natural boke was on the cards. The poet engaged me in snide conversation and told me many times of his own prowess and how beloved he was of long-winded, two-faced, phoney, pain-in-the-arse television producers. His monkey picked at his nose.

Have you read my collection? he asked.

I tried to read your collection, I replied, but I think you can't write for toffee.

The poet sucked his cigarette and the ape grunted. All I remember is gazing at the offensively scarlet jacket which clothed the peacock and suddenly there was a gurgle deep within me. In seconds the two of them were dripping in the most vile and unpleasant boke –

Put that in your pipe and smoke it! I said.

The barman applauded and presented me with a gin and tonic on the house.

Those two guys are complete tossers, he assured me, and they've been drinking slops all night.

You've hit the nail on the head there, I said.

I'm telling you this purely by way of an example of the power that had taken hold of me. When the boke came, for whatever reason, there was nothing I could do. It was coming and hell nor high water couldn't stop it. I boked in The Palace,

The Norseman, The Stag's Head (in the back), The POD, The Auld Dubliner, An Béal Bocht, The Abbey Theatre, Trinity College, The Irish Museum of Modern Art, Sandymount Strand, The Ferryman – the whole shooting gallery.

I feared that it was a physical manifestation of my corruption. Such was the rot creeping through every artery, vein and capillary that it was beginning to congeal in the very bile of my gut. I boked the length and breath of Dublin like it was going out of fashion – (fuckin' Dostoevsky, says you!) God forgive me – I even boked at a Liam Óg Ó Floinn gig in Whelans.

Oh I boked all over the shop – Stephen's Green, in the Dodder, in the Royal Canal, Landsdowne Road, Pembroke Road, Strand Road, the Coombe, the National Concert Hall, the Kerlin Gallery, Tosca, Montrose, O'Connell Bridge, Captain America's, the Virgin Megastore, the DART, the Towers, the Olympia etc. etc. etc. You name it – I boked in it, from it or over it.

And this is where this tale takes a very sinister turn. One fine summer's day as the blackbirds were singing along the banks of the canal, I was suddenly attacked by the digs in the ribs. The inevitable boke followed and as I lay face down in the damp dockens and attended my own recovery, I heard my name being called. At once I recognised it as the hybrid drawl of Dwight Bud Belmondo. I believed myself delirious as I looked up to find him standing there, my old boozing companion from New York and the man who had killed the third of our trinity Flaco John James Joseph McHugh.

Bastard! I spat.

OK so I killed the guy, he said with his eyes shut. It's a long story.

Well I don't want to hear it. I ought to kill you myself! I

never liked you! You're a phoney and you're a creep! You've got a lot of nerve, Bud!

He sat down beside me and put his head in his hands.

I guessed that you'd be in Ireland and I knew you wouldn't go back to your folks in this state. You were easy enough to find – everybody knows you here. You're becoming a bit of a tourist attraction.

I was astonished at my own apathy. Here was the guy who had stabbed Flaco to death and left him bleeding on a New York sidewalk – a million miles from the damp, shiny streets of home and the Mount Lourdes girls and the big yellow buses. I just seemed to be without any feeling. I knew then that I was in a bad way. There were no decent feelings left in me. I was like a dead man.

Bud straightened up and said:

I want to see Flaco again.

You what?

I want to see him again!

Yeah right.

Bud spat in the canal and put his hands in his pockets and spat again and looked to the sky and looked around and sat down and ran his hands through his hair and spat in the grass -

I want to see him again, he repeated. Have you ever heard of necromantic constraint?

Well of course I had heard of necromantic constraint! In my studies of the old texts I had many times come across the work of Doctor Dee and Edward Kelley (and mark you that appellation!) Doctor Dee believed that he could conjure angels and Kelley not only went along with that but he was an alchemist as well. But then, as I told Bud, I was neither Faust nor some half-assed Renaissance magus so if he thought I was going to necromantically constrain anyone, he was way off beam.

You're way off beam, I said.

Bud shook a little and rubbed his eyes with his cuffs.

I need to talk to him, man! I really need to talk to him!

I thought about it for a while and I suppose I figured well, at least it's something new, and with the indifference of an Algerian goalkeeper on a beach, I agreed to play ball. In any case, hadn't I damn all else to lose in terms of my alleged immortal soul? The following day we were on an Odyssean Ulsterbus to the county of Fermanagh. Late that evening, we slipped quietly into Enniskillen and, taking great care to ensure that my mother was unaware of my presence in town, we headed directly to the boneyard and prepared ourselves for what would follow.

Necromantic constraint is nothing to be at, and for this reason alone I choose not to divulge to you the method I employed. Suffice to say that we positioned ourselves fornenst the headstone of our subject and that the graveyard was pitch.

Are you sure, I asked, that you want to do this?

Sure as shootin', said Bud.

I took out the chalk and the candles. Bud lit the candles and I commenced to draw circles and symbols and names like Rex and Rael and Tarniel. I'll say no more because you'll be at it yourselves. The invocation was made and moments later Flaco John James Joseph McHugh appeared at his own headstone wearing his own winding cloth. He looked just as I remembered him only he was greyish and transparent.

Oh man! shouted Bud. This is too much!

Shut your mouth, you Yankee asshole! I quipped.

Man, is it him?

Who in hell's blazes do you think it is? It's his grave isn't it?

Flaco is it you? asked Bud, his voice full of trembling.

Yes it is me, Flaco John James Joseph McHugh. You're some pup! Stabbing me like that when I wasn't ready. All I did was say that Johnny Cash could sing none and neither he can!

Flaco, said Bud, forgive me, man.

Fuck away off! It was very sore!

I interrupted:

Flaco it's me!

I might have known you'd end up in something like this. It's nothing to be at!

Ah, what odds? I replied.

Flaco seemed to smile.

Did you hear the one about the fella at the Olympics and this guy comes over to him and says are you a pole-vaulter? The fella looks at him and says no, I'm a German, but how did you know my name?

That's a good 'un, fucksake! I laughed.

I took some time to study the general demeanour of my ghostly friend. I was far from afraid of him but I was a trifle nervy. I'd had little previous experience of apparitions and up until now I neither believed nor didn't believe. I was now facing the facts. Sure I had heard of Marley's ghost and the ghost that was seen by Athenodorous and Hamlet's father's ghost and the Cooneen ghost. And then there was the Headless Horseman of Sleepy Hollow and the ghost of Philinnion, daughter of Charito and Demostratus, who kept lepping into bed with her beloved Machetes – her being six months dead being of little consequence. At home there was the Castle Ghost, the Ghost of the Back Lough and the Ghost of Peggy the Bull. Oh it was ghosts a go-go right enough – but this was the first time I found myself in conversation with one.

Flaco had an air of calm and peace about him although he seemed a little uncomfortable to have been called from his place. He was doing his best to be nice to me but he wouldn't give Bud the time of day.

Get that gobshite out of my way! was his usual refrain.

Do you know what? said the ghost of Flaco, that the noble philosopher Sallust wasn't far off the mark with his doctrine of metempsychosis. There's some quare smart men about.

Bud was tearing at his hair and he suddenly hunkered down in front of Flaco —

Please man! Talk to me! I'm sorry man! I swear! I never meant it!

G'way and shite! snapped Flaco.

Aye, g'way and shite! I echoed.

Please Flaco! I'm a changed man. I have reformed! I am a sinner no more! I met Jesus in prison!

What was he in for! screamed Flaco, roaring with laughter.

Please man!

Anyway, you should still be inside!

Bud hung his head.

I was sprung. I escaped. The voice told me to break out and come here and seek your forgiveness. Can you forgive me, man?

So here I was in a Fermanagh graveyard with a ghost and an escaped con. Isn't it weird the situations you can get into?

Flaco addressed me again:

I meet Elvis regular. He's a hoot!

You've met Elvis?

Indeed and I have. He's the best of crack. Salt of the earth — no airs nor nothing. A gentleman!

So what's the story about the Million Dollar Quartet?

Ah ha! shouted Flaco, what did I tell you? Johnny Cash

was in the toilets the whole time! Of course the Yank here wouldn't believe me. Damn sure I made a beeline for Elvis and asked him straight-up: was Johnny Cash in the bogs or what? Elvis said sure he was. Ah Elvis is the best of a creatur! His people are all from Fermanagh – way, way back.

Bud was in tears.

I'm sorry Flaco, I'm sorry.

Flaco was not amused.

How many times did you stab me you mad bastard? What was it? Thirty times! You call that an accident? Listen boy, you should be running a motel in a Hitchcock film. You're a liability! As far as I'm concerned you can go jump in the lough. It's over there, mate, and seeing as your listening to voices you might as well listen to this one: go on! Jump in the lough!

Bud turned and ran down the hill, all the time screaming about repentance and sin. He disappeared into the darkness but still I could hear the crunch of his feet on pebbles and grass. The sound became softer as he entered the boggy, rushy land beside the lough. The sounds disappeared and all went quiet. Myself and Flaco listened. All was still but for the call of a corncrake and the whistle of a curlew. Suddenly there was the slightest of splashes – just as if a pike had rolled – and Bud was gone.

Flaco laughed.

Bud Belmondo swims with the fishes!

He was a bad shite! I said.

Indeed and he was!

Flaco told me a couple of jokes and asked me never to necromantically constrain him ever again. I agreed with my whole heart. I asked Flaco for help and all he could do was tell me the same stuff that Frank the priest had told me. It was all about faith, good works and grace.

He advised me to return to the pipes and to keep Liam Óg Ó Floinn at the forefront of my consciousness. He told me that on no account was I to pursue Niamh of the Golden Hair because it would end badly and he warned me very gravely that both Paddy Roberts and the Devil himself were after my hide. I took all of this on board, ran it up my mental flagpole and saluted it. I said my farewells to my dead friend and an empty cold breeze shot through the graveyard and up the back of my shirt. In a moment Flaco John James Joseph McHugh was gone.

I walked slowly towards the moonslicked water and listened to the nightnoises of frogs and birds. It was a quiet and beautiful night and I had never felt more alone in my life. I released a row-boat from its moorings and rowed in the near pitch darkness right through the town, past my own mother's house and out into the Lower Lough. There I would find some rest, far from all temptation and occasions of sin. Perhaps there on an island of bluebells and wild garlic I might find some peace.

SIXTEEN

My first night alone on the island of Inisthoin was a long and lonely one. Just a mile away, my mother was on her two knees saying the novenas and lighting the candles – all in the hope that her wayward son would return to his prayers and a fattened calf. I pictured the house and my room as I had left it for school that morning of the Battle of the Box Alley. Ah those innocent days – the little Arsenal strip, the statue of Saint Martin de Porres of Peru, the spacehopper and a bag of marbles. I longed to be there but it was now too late and I left my thoughts with the leaves that floated on the waters of the Erne. I was a condemned man – condemned to a world of my own creation – a world of which I thought I alone was master. The sin of pride is a deadly thing and I was full of deadly grief.

I did not sleep that first night. I stood on lonely watch awaiting the sun. When it came, it was the holiest of dawns and a sight that every man, woman and beast should see with their two eyes. A pall of muslin mist and a murmuring wash of rushes – the perfect golden sphere of sun floating steadily in its own arc. The silence of the darkness ending and a thousand birds showering the warming air with their songs. First just one and then the sudden tumult of a thousand curlews, lapwings, buntings and warblers. The sonic echo of baldicoots cut though the mist and the swallows appeared from nowhere to skim the waters for early flies. Great Canada geese whooped and clattered through the trees and launched themselves on the lough, their great feet spread out before them. Everything became alive in an instant: fish rose, flies droned and herons silently circled their nests above.

I stood on the shore, the gentle lapping of the lough almost lulling me to sleep, the rushes gently swaying, the faint sound of cattle in the distance. I surveyed what was indeed my world and soon I was back at the trout-tickling and the root-foraging. Before long I was sitting down to a fine meal of fish in wild garlic and the sweetest of nettle tea. As I ate, a sapphire dragon-fly landed momentarily on my forearm and this I took as a sign of benediction. I might remain here and take my ease. Perhaps here on this quiet island, surrounded by nature, I might find grace itself.

In a gesture of repentance I slid my boat into the water and watched it drift silently into the mist. By this action I left myself alone, isolated and completely at the mercy of whatever it is that runs this universe and doles out grace. I believed myself a changed man.

I made for myself a shelter of hazel, flag and fern and fashioned for myself a bed of birch boughs, saplings and fragrant rushes. This was all done after the fashion of the heroes of old who would often be out all night in pursuit of the caribou and elk. This complete I lay down among the pheasants and feral goats and slept for many hours. As the greengolden light dappled my restful face I dreamt of the paradise I might have found.

When I awoke and found myself staring at the very grass and orchids I had been dreaming of, I was at once filled with happiness and peaceful bliss. I could ask for no more than this and as I listened to the sounds around me I felt as if I was a part of the earth itself. All around me, badgers, stoats, rabbits, hares, foxes, hedgehogs, shrews, voles and chipmunks rustled through the undergrowth, uneasy about their island's new inhabitant. Never had I been closer – never had I been further from home.

The days progressed quietly and gracefully and, inspired by the monks who had lived here before me, I attempted meditation and prayer. These emaciated holy men would sit perched on top of round towers for twenty years or more in a meditative state of trance, the painful point of the tower inflicting unthinkable pain in the regions of their backsides. These men filled me with inspiration and I resolved to get closer to the realities of life.

This was a period of great hope and I was singularly unaffected by temptations of any kind. Neither lust nor greed came near me and for a few foolish days I began to believe that I had escaped from my own weakness. I was, alas, much mistaken.

My rest grew uneasy as the weeks progressed. I began to feel that there were eyes on me apart from the those belonging to the creatures of the wood. When a fern moved I began to question the cause and found myself uttering, 'Who's there?' There was never any response, but why, I asked myself, was I feeling this uneasiness? The reasons are about to become obvious.

I awoke one morning on my fresh bed of birch, hazel, ferns, flags, lichen and moss and came out of a dream of horses' hooves. I was confused as to whether the sound of the horse was dream, half-dream or waking dream and my eyes rolled around and my ears stretched to the air outside. Suddenly there came to me an unmistakable equine snort. There was without question a horse at my front door and as I scrambled out my face found itself pressed against the fine fetlocks of a grand white stallion of many hands.

As I arose I remarked a drape of fine red silk, embroidered with golden thread and as I panned across and upwards along the horse's flank I encountered the fair white foot of a woman hanging gently in a golden stirrup set with diamonds, rubies, emeralds and pearls. The foot extended into the folds of the red silk and my eyes went onwards and upwards along the curves of hidden thigh until they met with the golden locks I knew at once. There gazing down at me were the green eyes I had dreamed of – they both belonged to Niamh of the Golden Hair!

Is mise Niamh, she smiled, I am Niamh. *Je m'appelle Niamh.*

I know well who you are, I said, and it is true that I love you more than life itself.

Tá 'fhios agam. I know. *Je sais.*

You are more beauteous than the melodious corncrake at midnight! More gorgeous than all the Roses of Tralee! More of a honey than a thousand Sharon Shannons! I love you like the stars, like the moon, like fresh trout on a wet morning in July and I want to live with you forever in the Land of the Good People!

Niamh of the Golden Hair smiled and threw back her head. For reasons of brevity I will précis her remarks because her insistence on using three languages becomes a tad much after a while. With no disrespect to the Old Tongue of the Gael or to the present tongue of the Gaul I shall henceforth report her remarks in *béarla*, English, *anglais*.

It is true, said Niamh of the Golden Hair, that you are in love with me and it is further true that I am in love with you.

It was I who brought you to this place and though you suspect that you drifted here by chance you are far from correct. It was I who guided your boat to this island because this is the ancient dwelling place of the ancient people of Ireland from whom you are descended. This is the place of your ancestors. This is the island of Inisthoin and you are welcome in this place.

But Niamh of the Golden Hair, I said, when we last spoke together in New York it was an incontestable fact that I could step no further towards that rhododendron bush because, as you said yourself in the sweetest voice, I was unworthy of you.

What you say is true, smiled Niamh of the Golden Hair, but it is a true bill that I have been keeping a fair green eye on you. There are signs my love that you are approaching readiness. Your preoccupations with modern religions and your old-hat remarks about sexual repression in a priest-ridden Ireland are most tiresome and outplayed but the fact remains that your present communion with nature and the old ways has shown a certain worthiness. Your saving grace, my love, is your *grá* for the pipes and your veneration of the one they call Ó Floinn.

Niamh of the Golden Hair, I gasped, let me go away with you now to the Land of the Good People and let us live there forever!

Niamh smiled.

There are things my love that you do not yet understand. Before you can ever come with me to my world there are three tasks which you must perform as proof of your worthiness and love for me. Once completed then you will come back with me to the Land of The Good People and there we will eat haunches of venison, drink wine and make much love on the carpet. I will be yours and will lie with you in the golden palaces of my land.

112

Niamh of the Golden Hair! I moaned, what is it that I must do? Tell me now so that I can complete these tasks post haste for it is true that there is an impatient lust growing in my limbs!

Niamh looked solemn.

You will have three tasks – one of agility, one of poetry-saying and one of battle. Only when all three are complete can we lie together before the hearth.

Name me my first task! I called, the task of agility!

Niamh raised her hand and said:

I have in my pocket a silver coin which is known in your world as a dime. It features a representation of one of your high kings known as FDR. I shall place this dime upon the ground and you shall dance upon it. If your foot strays once from the dime you will have failed the test and will be lost to me forever.

Show me the dime! I said, and surely I will dance upon it!

With that a great music arose around me. It was a class of hornpipe and with great heroic agility and balance I began to dance upon the dime. Such dancing was never before seen and not once did my rigid arms flap about about me. I leapt as high as fifty men and kicked as high as fifty more, each time landing on my two big toes on the head of FDR. For seven days and seven nights I bucklepped and capered and for all the pains in the calves of my legs I kept my eyes fixed upon my love, Niamh of the Golden Hair.

On the seventh of the seven days the music suddenly stopped and I collapsed in a heap in the garlic and thistles. Not for a single moment had my chin dropped. Niamh of the Golden hair was pleased.

You have pleased me greatly and you have fulfilled the first of the three tasks. Now you may rest for three days and three nights and I shall attend to the pains in the calves of your legs.

And Niamh of the Golden hair went off to gather herbs and spices.

On the third day of the third night my love stood before me and said –

Now you must fulfil the second of the three tasks. This is the task of poetry-saying and you must please me with words and the sweetness of your voice. You must compose for me a poem in honour of my beauty and this you must do off the top of you head without recourse to notes, reciting it as you make it up. It must not rhyme and must contain no more than ten lines. If your poem pleases me then you will have completed the second test and will be that much closer to the making of love in the silken bedrooms of the other world.

Niamh of the Golden Hair, I said, you are so beautiful to my gaze that such a task is simple to me. I could spout poetry till the cows come home and go away again. Now I will attempt with some confidence your second task.

Oh Niamh of the Golden Hair! I began:

> You are the bee's knees.
> You are the cat's pajamas.
> You are the Road to God Knows Where.
> You are the butter in my bap.
> You are the lost chord.
> You are the Fifth Beatle.
> You are the Back of Beyond.
> You are the Chateauneuf du Pape.
> You are a dish.

Niamh of the Golden hair smiled.

You have pleased me greatly by the power of your poetry-spouting. Such is your power with words and such is the sweetness in your voice that I feel I cannot refuse you. There is however one final and very grave task. It is the task of battle and war-fighting. Should you complete this task we will go to my land on the back of my horse and we will eat and drink our fill and we will lie in a sweaty heap until morning.

Tell me Niamh of the Golden Hair, I groaned, what must I do for it is true that I am overcome with indescribable urges!

Niamh's face once again grew solemn.

My love, there is an evil spirit on your tail. He has followed you around the world, to New York, Paris and Rome. On each occasion he has just failed to ensnare you and now my beautiful dime-dancing, spouter of verse, it is your destiny to face your enemy here on this island. Here you will fight him to the death and only when his body is floating towards Belleek in a bloody heap will your task be complete.

O Niamh of the Golden Hair! I said, if I am to win your love there is nothing in heaven or earth that I would fear! Who is this evil spirit whom I must beat up?

He is a fearsome spirit come from hell with all the powers of darkness at his command. He is a fat bald thing and you once knew him as Paddy Roberts!

O my prophetic soul! I yelled, Paddy Roberts, teacher of English! Behold the creatur!

Yes, said Niamh of the Golden Hair, it is indeed the one you defeated once before at the great Battle of the Box Alley. That was, to tell the truth, the first time that I regarded your grotesquely distorted visage and I confess that I have loved you ever since. I fear for you now, my love, because Paddy Roberts is the baddest of eggs and he means to avenge his death here on this verdant shore. In two days he will be here and you

115

must prepare yourself for the mother of all battles.

On the second morning of the second day the great crows of battle, the Morrigu and Badb, began to circle above and I knew that this was the day of my destiny. This would be the day when I would see again the awful pasty face of Paddy Roberts, the twisted teacher of so long ago. I was far from afraid of Paddy Roberts but I now feared the powers he had at his command. This would be a deadly foe and even the most warped of spasms might not be enough against incarnate evil.

I no longer saw the badgers and shrews and foxes and goats. I no longer heard the curlew and snipe and warbler and coot. All I could hear were the great crows of death above me and the sound of Niamh of the Golden Hair whistling the saddest of tunes as she washed her feet in the Erne.

There was a deadly silence over the lough as I awaited the first sighting of Paddy Roberts the teacher from Hell. Niamh of the Golden Hair took up a position, seated upon her horse, quite some distance away on a low mound and there she gently lilted tunes to stir my blood for the battle to come. I was sick with the wait and it occurred to me that it had been a not inconsiderable time since I last boked, tormented by whatever evil was digging me in the ribs. It occurred to me also that I was deeply in love with Niamh of the Golden Hair and that she might have replaced the pipes and, God preserve us, maybe even Ó Floinn himself as the object of my obsessional obsession. Many thoughts raced through my head as I readied myself to fight or die.

All was silent but for the two crows of battle and my wait was not long. As I strained my eyes to see, a great black boat began to take its form in the mist. Like some serpent from the glarry depths it sailed towards me and there right enough, as large as life, was Paddy Roberts.

His face was twisted and scarlet and his clothes hung about him in rags and scraps of fur. His great hairy shoulders heaved in rage.

I'll make short work of a pup like you! he yelled.

His voice echoed his malice across the lough and a thousand birds scattered to the air.

I am Paddy Roberts and I am an evil bastard! You didn't like me when I was alive but wait until you get a load of me now! I have all the powers of hell at my command for I have found my place! And it is a place full of schoolteachers! You are dead meat my pipe-squeezing bucko!

Paddy Roberts! I shouted across the waters, you are still the lardy-faced heap of shite that you always were and I am not afraid of you or your powers! I killed you before and once again I will go into heroic warp spasm and kick your arse! What's more you can spell none!

We shall see! Oh yes we're all very smart today aren't we?

Come over here and fight like a man, you big shite!

I can stand here all day you know, replied Paddy Roberts.

Don't talk that teacher crap to me! You're a companion prince in hell and I am of the Tuatha Dé Danaan. It is true that I love Niamh of the Golden Hair and it is also true that if I slay you this day I will have completed the third of three great tasks. This done I will live with my beloved forever in a land of venison, vino and sexual congress!

Oh do you really think so? sneered Roberts. We'll see who's the big man now!

With that, Paddy Roberts raised his two blue and white arms and ascended with great fury into the air. A great wind arose and the ether was ablaze with chalkdust and dandruff.

By the powers of darkness, he screamed in a demented voice,

I'll kill you dead!

Kiss my ass! I suggested as a more likely alternative.

No sooner had the words left my lips than my face began to contort and my eyes bulged. My hair stood on end and my body assumed grotesque forms. The warp spasm was on me! I let out a great hero yell and myself and Roberts were once more engaged in heroic battle-frenzy high up in the air.

What exactly happened I cannot remember but you can gauge by the fact that I am telling this tale that I beat him up and down the yard. In my warp spasm I lose my mind and when I come out of the warp spasm I cannot remember where I left it. For a true record of what happened, of all the shaking and gnashing and biting and hacking and strangling and ripping and tearing and gouging and battering and thumping, I can tell you nothing other than relay to you now the sweet song that was sung by Niamh of the Golden Hair to praise my success. Picture the scene: I am lying in the rushes, the water steaming around me as my heroic battle frenzy is cooled. For six days and six nights I have lain there boiling Lough Erne dry with the heat of my battle rage. The Morrigu and Badb have departed and the carcass from hell is floating to Belleek. Only Niamh of the Golden Hair remains, waiting for me to regain my natural form so that she can embrace me and put me on the back of her horse. As she waits she sings this sweet fairy song:

> While going the road to sweet Athy,
> Hurroo! hurroo!
> While going the road to sweet Athy,
> Hurroo! hurroo!
> While going the road to sweet Athy,
> A stick in my hand and a drop in my eye,
> A doleful damsel I heard cry:

'Och, Johnny, I hardly knew ye!
Fling your beavers aloft!
Fling your beavers aloft!
My darling dear you look so queer,
Och, Johnny, I hardly knew ye!'

Oh, he killed Paddy Roberts,
Hurroo! Hurroo!
Knocked him dead with the flat of his hand!
Hurroo! Hurroo!
He twisted the head off the teacher he slew;
He tore off his arms for something to do.
A doleful damsel I heard cry:
'Och Johnny I hardly knew ye!
Fling your beavers aloft!
Fling your beavers aloft!
My darling dear you look so queer,
Och, Johnny, I hardly knew ye!'

Tore lumps of his hair,
Hurroo! hurroo!
Kicked shins and headbutted,
Hurroo! hurroo!
Pushed his head under water
To finish the slaughter.
I heard a doleful damsel cry:
'Och, Johnny, I hardly knew ye!
Fling your beavers aloft!
Fling your beavers aloft!
My darling dear, you look so queer,
Och, Johnny, I hardly knew you.'

SEVENTEEN

*P*ermission to speak?

Granted.

Would you mind just holding your ruminatory horses for just one tick?

I'm listening so I am.

May I ask you a pertinent question?

Fire ahead.

Are you on drugs or what?

That, sir, is an impertinent question and I resent it greatly. The facts of my existence at this time may well be hard to credit but I assure you of their veracity.

So let me get this straight: leaving aside all the smoking and boking and acting the clown; leaving aside all the pipe-stealing and badger visions; leaving aside all the necromantic constraint and the doctrine of metempsychosis; leaving aside the dime-dancing and fairy-talking; you now tell me that you have once again undergone heroic warp spasm and killed (for the second time, mark you) an English teacher from Hades known as Paddy Roberts?

That's it exactly and it is a grand cake, Nora.

To think that once I tried to guide you in the area of apple-nyucking and girl-snogging! Those innocent days when you toked and sipped! Look at you now! A grievous sinner all but in league with the Devil himself! Murder! Robbery! Drunkenness! Fornication! Sloth! Pride and paganism! You are a lost cause, my boy! Go with the fairy-woman for that is where you now belong! You are lost without coordinates! You are up the sinful Swannee without a moral paddle! What would the nuns in first class or the nuns in your mother's first class make of you now?

I care not a jot for the Sisters of Mercy nor for your scruples.

What about your mortal soul? You must think of this! Think of hell! Think of that place from whence Paddy Roberts came to pursue you to New York, Paris, Rome and finally to this accursed island of Inisthoin! You must dwell on the sufferings of hell and attempt now to escape them! In all thy works remember thy last end and thou shall never sin! Enter ye in at the narrow gate; for wide is the gate and broad is the way that leads to destruction, and many they are that go in thereat. How narrow is the gate and strait is the way that leadeth to life; and few there are who find it! It is the diligent servant who shall enter into the joy of his Lord; but the unprofitable servant shall be cast into the exterior darkness where there shall be weeping and wailing and gnashing of teeth!

And you believe all this?

Each will suffer in proportion to his sins and to his abuse of the graces offered to him. God will render to every man acccording to his works!

And what about this Devil character? According to Frank he is in me already!

This would come as no surprise for it is the Devil who has guided you along your way thus far. From that first drag on that first fag and those twelve pints of stout and that accursed temptress from Baden-Baden, you have been holding on to the shirt-tails of Satan for many a year and you are now beyond all.

Did you hear about the dyslexic Devil worshipper?

Naw I did not.

He sold his soul to Santa!

Boys, but that's a good one!

I tell you now that I have my Niamh of the Golden Hair. I have completed the three tasks she set me and now she is mine. I will go with her on the back of her horse to the Land of the Good People and there we will lie down on the best of rugs. I will have no need of you nor your fearsome tales of hell and damnation. I will live forever in robes of silk embroidered with finest gold. Around my neck a silver torc set with emeralds and precious stones from Africk's shore. I will not hear you there and you will fade away from me. Your questions and concerns will no longer put a damper on the happiness that is mine! Get behind me, Conscience! Take a hike!

I looked around and there was Niamh of the Golden Hair. A great light shone about her as she sat astride her great white horse.

My love, she said, you have completed the three tasks I set you and you have been cooled from your warp spasm by the soothing glarry waters of the damp Erne. Now it is time for us to depart so that I can fulfil my part of the bargain and take you with me to my country where we will eat, drink and make love like two Ballyshannon rabbits. Lep up here upon the back of my horse and we shall leave this place.

With one flash of my great teeth I was up on the back of her horse with my hands clasped tightly against the slim warm stomach I could feel beneath the silk. I buried my face in her golden locks and inhaled the fragrant fragrance of her hair.

Heigho, Silver! I shouted. Geronimo!

And away off with the two of us, the hooves of the great white horse barely touching the water and throwing out behind us the finest of spray. The golden hair of Niamh streamed out behind her and and I felt a rush of magical excitement as we rode headlong into the damp whiteness and roaring wind.

Suddenly all about us there was a hero-light and birds of all descriptions began to shoot out of nowhere and flash by our faces – geese in great spiralling flight, cormorants carving low about around us and swallows in slalom through the hurtling legs of our steed.

We are on our way now, my love, said Niamh of the Golden Hair in her customary three languages.

Indeed and we are! I shouted in her ear and I pressed my mouth against her wet cheek.

We flew on and on into the mist, the horse carrying us towards some invisible destination. With my hands about her waist I could feel every shimmering breath of my beloved Niamh and I was filled with a great longing. Not a baldie's notion had I where we were. Was the horse running headlong across the surface of the lough itself? Or were we under the lough and descending into its glarry depths? Or were we high above its broad expanse and somewhere in the skies above the Navar viewpoint? It is true that I was transported in manys a way.

Oh Niamh of the Golden Hair, I yelled above the ferocious wind, where are we?

We are almost there my love! Soon this mist will clear and you will see for the first time the Land of the Good People and you will enter there and be with me forever in sweet ecstatic congress.

By the hokey! I yahooed. Ye ho!

Author's Note
Your man in *A Bout de Souffle* was called Jean-Paul Belmondo.
End of Author's Note

When at last the great Erne mists cleared, I found a great need to cling ever closer to the warm hips of my love for it is no lie that when we emerged from our clouds far, far up in the blue-black Fermanagh sky, such was the great shock at our altitude and the further realisation that our blue-black skies had turned to Aegean blue that I let a gulder out of me that seemed to scare the horse. His eyes rolled and he took to galloping ever faster across the nothingness of the heavens.

'Tis a flying horse that we are upon! I gasped.

It is true that this horse is capable of flight. You will find that many things are possible in the land which lies below us. Yes, my love, take a look because yonder is the Land of the Good People!

Niamh of the Golden Hair stretched her graceful hand out before her and suddenly a great music drifted in on the wind. I recognised it at once as the music of the *sí* and happiness enveloped my pipe-loving heart. It was a mad frantic music that might have been beaten out by the blurring golden horseshoes of our horse and it was a music like I had never heard before.

As if to welcome us, a host of great coloured birds of a thousand pigments and hues began to weave about our heads – scarlet flamingoes, hummingbirds, lyre birds, macaws and corncrakes – all of them whistling the great tunes of the *sí* and showering us with the petals of golden whinbushes.

As our horse began its descent I could see stretched before me the vast fertile plains of the otherworld, winding blue rivers and palaces of gold. It was indeed a beautiful place of riches and wealth, the greenest of greens, the reddest of reds and the bluest of blues. I was like a pig in shite.

Behold the beyond and the back of beyond! said Niamh of

the Golden Hair. All of this is yours! And behold yon palace yonder where all of this is also yours. She gestured towards her own beauteous frame and smiled.

Let us hurry then my love because I wish to complete all immigration formalities with the minimum of fuss and palaver! We shall take a taxi to your place and make exotic love upon the kitchen table! How does that grab ye?

That sounds like a fair notion, smiled my Niamh of the Golden Hair. Grand cake Nora!

With that our horse came to a stop in a great wheatfield spilling over with wheat the height of sixteen men. Dragonflies the size of Ford Cortinas hovered about and outsize curlews made noises that would deaven you.

Walk with me through this field, said Niamh of the Golden Hair, and I will take you to my place.

This was the grandest land and I was at once filled with ease, contentment and notions of permanence. All other thoughts deserted me. I wanted nothing, feared nothing and cared not a hair for questions of life, death, the universe and sin. I was beyond that because this was the back of beyond and I was therefore and without question, beyond all.

As we emerged from the wheatfield we turned onto a pathway paved with precious metals all inlaid with rubies and pearls. At the side of the road, forty badgers all with pipes under their oxters took care to salute us and welcome us to the Land of the Good People. They did so in four languages – the Old Tongue, English, French and a form of speech I presumed to be Badger. At the end of this jewelled pathway we came to a great crossroads and here our horse came to a stop.

My love, said Niamh of the Golden Hair, here is the Great Crossroads of the Heroic Notions. There are four roads here –

one road is the road we have just travelled and if you choose it now you may return to your world of bad weather, bad eggs and the sexual repression often dealt with in your works of literature. The road straight ahead is the road to my home. There we will live together, eating and drinking of the best, spending a lot of time in my goosedown bed and never growing old. The road to our left is the Great Bendy Road of Temptation. At the end of this road there is a set of the finest uilleann pipes carved from the best of ebony and he who plays these pipes will be the greatest piper ever heard in either of our worlds. The road to the right is a road no one here has ever travelled for it is the Great Hard Road. Nobody knows where it goes but some say it is a ring-road which joins the Great Bendy Road of Temptation just at the spot where the set of pipes await the tempted. You must choose and you must make this choice now! I must warn you also my love that once travelled, none of these roads can be travelled again in any direction.

I surveyed the roads, discounting first the road I had travelled; not for me the bad conscience and bad eggs of my own world. Then I cast my eyes to the Great Hard Road and that, too, I discounted; not for me the sin and evil of drinking, smoking, snorting, brawling, toilet-sleeping, gutter-crawling, women-chasing and door-knocking. The Great Bendy Road of Temptation promised to make me the greatest piper of all – something I would once have given my right arm for. In this world however the temptation had no pull on me; not for me the sins of pride and envy. I would learn the pipes in my own time and I had a genuine eternity in which to do so. Finally, I looked to the road ahead, the road to Niamh's place, this was the road for me and no bones about it.

Niamh of the Golden Hair, I announced, I choose the road

126

ahead for it is true that none of these other throughways hold any interest for me. Take me to your goosedown bed and we shall live forever in happiness and health!

You have chosen well, smiled Niamh, and the horse carried us onwards at a frustratingly slow pace.

Much love was made for six days and six nights and I began to question whether or not the entire concept of sexual repression is in fact a complete invention of the Irish novelist – there was neither hilt nor hare of it about the two of us. At the end of the sixth night of the sixth day we lay there in an exhausted heap of sweaty limbs and I took an outrageous notion of a chicken curry, a foodstuff alas unavailable in the Land of the Good People.

As I lay there contemplating the wonders of the chicken curry it began to dawn upon me that I was already thinking of my own world. For all the love-making, venison and fine wines I was already desiring something else – something that was once only a phone call and delivery charge away. Niamh of the Golden Hair awoke from her sweet slumbers and sensed my thoughts.

Oh my love, she said, it is true that we have made the greatest of all love for six days and six nights with only the odd intermission for the purposes of venison eating, wine drinking and cramp-fixing. But is is true now my love that there is a sadness coming over you and I fear that there is something you desire that is not mine to give. What ails you my love?

Niamh of the Golden Hair, I said tenderly, I want a chicken curry.

Niamh sat up in the bed with a look of disdain spreading all over her Belleek china face.

A chicken curry, is it? A chicken curry, no less? I'll give you chicken curry!

A great wind arose about me and a darkness overcame me as if in a faint. When I awoke I was lying nude as a bee at the very crossroads I had encountered only six days and six nights before. Around me, forty badgers were laughing forty badger laughs and a voice came to me from the skies above. It was the voice of Niamh of the Golden Hair:

My love, you have failed me and now you lie there nude as a bee and I find you a disagreeable sight. You chose well at these crossroads but now I know that you were driven entirely by lust and desire. Now that you have had your way for six days and six nights all you desire is a fancy foodstuff catchpenny unavailable in the Land of the Good People and I can only assume that you desire your own world more than you desire mine. I would have given everything to you and we would have lived happily for ever in my goosedown bed. But oh no! This was not enough for you! You wanted more! In the guilty exhaustion of your love-making you thought not of holding me or stroking my hair; instead you thought of escape, solitude and culinary congress with pieces of curried poultry! You are not worthy of me and we must part!

How can I go from you Niamh of the Golden Hair, I implored. How can I ever stray from you my love?

But she was gone – taking the forty badgers with her. I got up on my knees and commenced to curse myself in the worst of bad temper. Once more I found myself surveying the crossroads and I remembered the words of Niamh of the Golden Hair: to take the road back to her goosedown bed was impossible, so too the road back to Inisthoin and the land of bad eggs. Each road she had said, once travelled could not be travelled again and that left only the two potential paths – the

Great Bendy Road of Temptation and the Great Hard Road and there was a strong chance that they were both part of the same circuitous route. I was banjaxed.

My fine fellow, might I interrupt?

Try stopping you!

May I commence with my customary interrogation?

Fire ahead.

Have you been drinking or taking hallucinogens, perhaps?

You believe nothing, sure you don't?

I believe in one God, the Father almighty, creator of heaven and earth – and so on.

Fair dues, so what do you want?

So you have two roads out of four and the two roads might the one road. Am I right so far?

You are so.

And the road on your left is the Great Bendy Road of Temptation and at the end of it there is a set of pipes that will make you the greatest piper in Christendom?

Indeed so.

The other road is the Great Hard Road and nobody knows what lies down that road except that it is bad business and might well be the highroad to hell itself. Am I right?

You're dead right.

Are you aware you're as nude as a bee?

I am aware of my condition.

Have you no shame?

No I have not.

What of your beloved Goldilocks?

She can go to pot!

Fickle, aren't we?

Bog off!

You might be glad of me, my boy – depending on what road you chose. You might be glad of an informed conscience to plot your way out of this one.

And which road do you recommend if you're so smart?

The one to the left will lead to destruction. You can go down that bendy road and pick up those pipes and be the greatest piper in the Milky Way. But it will be a fact that you will be playing accursed pipes and you will be a disgrace to the piping profession and you will never be a match for the noble Ó Floinn – he of the honourable and immobile expression. If you take the other road, the hard road – and you have no choice – you can use whatever grace you have to defeat whatever befalls you. I will assist.

So I am to follow my conscience for the first time? And I am to follow it down the Great Hard Road?

It might do you no harm! Just follow me the once and we'll see what happens. Anyway, you have damn all choice in the matter! That bendy one is bad news and you know it!

Dejectedly and nude as a bee, I walked down the Great Hard Road and began to boke ferociously until I was dry-boking on my hands and knees, barking like a dog.

EIGHTEEN

O f the many and varied forms of boke known to the animal kingdom it is perhaps the dry-boke which is the biggest snooker. It is a boke like any other in many respects save for one major discrepancy – the boke does not produce boke. In other words, the verb does not produce the noun and therefore a body is linguistically as well as physically jiggered.

Much like the bokes of Paris and the famous National Gallery of Ireland boke when I effected criminal damage to Joseph Haverty's 'Blind Piper', this current spate of attacks was in each case prefaced by the customary punches and digs in the ribs. Such was the ferocity of these inflictions that I considered myself under serious attack from a force unseen. I was in the straightest and direst of dire straits.

As I lay there in the recovery position I was fair desperate. I had made every error imaginable and I deemed that I had now found my own hell. Here I was finally in a literal under-world: all roads but the one I travelled was closed to me and I was cut off from all pleasures. I would wander this ring-road forever, boking dry bokes, tormented and tortured by whatever evil had a hold of me. I began to despair and consider it too late for prayer, redemption, salvation and grace. I would follow this, my only road and see where it finally led. This is the road I had set out upon on some unspecified time on some unspecified day. I would never know, nor can anyone tell me, when it all started; but this, I began to credit, was where it would end.

I travelled the Great Hard Road for thirty-three days and thirty-three nights. I had no food, no drink and no thoughts of anything but the pleasures I had left behind and the suffering that awaited me. On the thirty-third night of the thirty third day I came to a door and a door within the door within the door. I opened the smallest of the doors and entered a room.

Like the Punt Club in Paris it was badly lit, all cherry red and black. I looked about me and fairly winced at what I saw: Lara Heidsieck at the bar, all dripping with pearls and lust, Dwight Bud Belmondo with eels in his pocket and a knife in his hand, a pompous poet with a peacock's tail and the legs of a scruff hanging out of his mouth, a German tourist in yellow wellies and a Camberwell carrot the length of your arm, Captain Martin of the New York Police Department sawing through sets of uilleann pipes with a hacksaw, Paddy Roberts reciting lumps of *Hamlet* and farting loudly, Roberto Baggio, Brigitte Bardot, two Swiss Guards, a skewered lamb, Kelley and Dee, Robert Johnson playing 'The Foxchase', Dostoevsky and a mass entanglement of faces I had known however briefly in the lost years of my blue period. In the corner a blind piper wearing only the one sock and sitting without the aid of a chair was playing 'The Wind that Shakes the Barley'.

Boys, you're in it now!

Well I didn't hang about I can tell you. I was out of there like a hare out of a trap and through another door which brought me back out onto a road, this time a brighter and more pleasant place and once again (and to my great relief) I found myself clothed in a suit made of polyester.

Man dear, do you know what I think it is?

What do you think it is?

I think you were given a glimpse of hell! Like the odd canonised character in the past you have been allowed to see what's in there in order that you might believe and change your ways. Was it St Teresa or St Catherine or some of them women? That'll sharpen you, my boy! All is not yet lost.

I walked further and further along this much more agreeable stretch of road and remarked on the primroses, violets, goose-grass, kidney vetch, wood anemone, lesser celandine, elderberry, coltsfoot, ladysmock, foxglove, deadly nightshade, cow parsley and giant hogweed. In the splendour of their smells I meditated upon the vision I had just received and was confused. I did not believe what I had seen to be hell for I had fought the Paddy Roberts man come from there and he had assured me that it was full of schoolteachers. That figured and I therefore surmised that what I had seen was in fact my own private mini-hell full of all the landmarks of my sinful, decadent and hedonistic existence. I resolved once more that, given the chance, I would reform, abandon all desires and no longer give myself to devils and succubi.

That's the fella!

I would return home and learn the pipes and give a concert for charity:

The World's Greatest Irish Piper and Bard of Erin

The most phenomenal artist living who plays the Irish pipes. It has been acknowledged by every nation in Europe that music was cultivated in Ireland when melody was scarcely known in other countries. Pope, the great poet, calls Ireland the mother of sweet singers, the truth of which is verified in a most natural gift to the manner born in the above great player, who will discourse the sweetest music ever heard, on Ireland's sweetest of national instruments, the Irish Pipes, carrying his audience with him at will with the plaintive strains of his dear native land.

Cold must the heart be,
And void of emotion,
That loves not the music
Acushla Machree.

During the evening the great piper will perform several imitations on the Irish Pipes, both ancient and modern musical, notably:

The Celebrated Foxhunt
A perfect imitation of the hounds in full cry:
Breaking Cover
Losing the Scent
In the Cornfield
On the Trail
The Death.

Cath Eachroma or the Battle of Aughrim
The Irish cries of the females for the dead friends and husbands found in the battlefield
Sounds of the Trumpets
Sarsfield's March to Limerick.
(The Irish cry is of remote antiquity, a period beyond the reach of memory).

The Old Man Rocking the Cradle

The great piper will imitate the human voice on the Irish
Pipes, making the instrument speak plain English in this old
Irish piece.

This concert will take place at The Technical College
Enniskillen at a date to be announced.
Tea and sandwiches will be served.
Tickets at usual outlets.
(All proceeds in aid of the Blind Pipers Fund of America.)

In my head I played my way through the programme and must
have cut a strange figure in my ill-fitting polyester suit and my
two elbows elbowing as I walked, my fingers playing on an
imaginary chanter and the whelps of the hounds coming from
my lips. I was however, content and briefly with purpose. At
each bend in the road I kept an eye out for some diversion but
none seemed to appear. I walked for twelve more days and
twelve more nights and on the twelfth night of the twelfth day
I came upon a door within a door within a door within a door.
I entered and found myself in a dark tunnel. I ceased my lilting
and a great nervousness surrounded me.

Be careful, now, boy!

Did you not hear that accursed woman Niamh of the Golden
Hair say that once travelled no road could be travelled again?
It should be clear to you from that statement that I cannot go
back the way I came and must therefore proceed with this
complicated door arrangement. I footered with assorted
doorknobs, latches, bolts and Chubb locks and emerged into a
small alley off Grafton Street, Dublin City, Ireland.

Well, raise my rent! You're out!

Huh! You haven't heard the half of it. I recognised at once

that the alley in which I found myself led to a nightclub to which I had been refused entry on numerous occasions. (As I have before indicated, my boking exploits were recorded the length and breadth of the fair city and my presence was invariably unwelcome in certain nightspots. My particular offence in this one was a newsworthy episode where I boked over a Rolling Stone.)

You're not shaggin' gettin' in here! declared one of many bouncers.

What appears to be the problem? I asked pleasantly.

Last time you were in here you threw up over certain valued customers and it's management policy that you are now barred! I'm sorry but you'll have to move along! You're not shaggin' gettin' in here! And stand back will you! I just got this suit dry-cleaned!

Bad and all as my need for a drink was I wasn't fussed where I got it. If they wouldn't let me in for fear I might hurl over a supermodel that was their look-out. I didn't even like the place anyway. I had just turned to leave when a long bony hand alighted on my shoulder –

It's all right, said a voice I didn't recognise. He's with me.

I turned to see who my sudden patron was and I found myself regarding a tall, completely bald, middle-aged man with an aquiline nose. He was wearing a long black coat with a velvet collar and I immediately took him to be someone involved in the music business.

I'll vouch for him, he said, nodding at me. He'll be OK.

Certainly, sir, grinned the bouncer and he stepped aside. With his hand on my arm, the stranger escorted me up the stairs and into the club. He had a table reserved for two and a bottle of Brut Reserve was already angled in an ice-bucket.

Sit down, won't you? he smiled.

Thanks, I said. You know I don't even like this place.

Yes, it can be a bit grim, he agreed.

I looked around and saw a lot of familiar faces and spotted a few personages that the management would not have liked me to boke over. I wanted to get out but felt I'd better humour the baldie man who had befriended me.

So here we are then, I said awkwardly.

Indeed and we are, he nodded. So you're the one who does all the vomiting?

Not if I can help it, I snapped.

Oh don't knock it; It's a skill! I was there when you decorated that poet and his accomplice. That was most agreeable.

I didn't like the way he laughed. It betrayed madness and I suddenly felt extremely uneasy. The more he spoke the more I realised that he knew far too much about me:

Still playing the pipes are you?

No, I gave it up as a bad job.

Enjoy Paris?

I said nothing. Maybe he was a policeman or a taxman or some old boozing partner who had been completely erased from my mind during all the madness?

I got angry:

Lookit, cleanhead, who the fuck are you?

I am the bee's knees, he replied.

I am the cat's pyjamas,

I am the Road to God Knows Where,

I am the butter in your bap,

I am the lost chord,

I am the Fifth Beatle,

I am the Back of Beyond,

I am the Chateauneuf du Pape,

I am a dish.

Yikes! Get away from him this minute!

Who in hell's blazes are you, you baldy bastard, I cried, grabbing him by his velvet lapels.

The stranger leaned forward, his eyes narrowed and grabbing my wrists with his two hands he leered:

I am the Devil himself.

Oh shite!

As soon as he said it, it was clear that he was indeed the Devil himself: Apollyon, Old Nick, Goatfeatures, Lucifer, the Archfiend, the Angel of the Bottomless Pit, the Old Gentleman, El Diablo, the Father of Lies, the Beast, the Serpent, the Prince of Darkness, Old Scratch, *An Drochrud.*

Old Horny!

Do you like the music in here? he grinned. I'm fond of U2 myself; wasn't *Zooropa* just divine?

I gazed into the bloodshot eyes of the Prince of Darkness and knew that I was in nothing short of a serious pickle.

NINETEEN

Here was a character to whom I had given little consideration at any stage in my life. I had debated the existence of God on countless occasions but never before had I seen this gentleman as a tangible element. Father Frank had told me that he believed in him and added quite confidently that the Devil dwelt in me. I of course had passed no remarks. To me these were the ravings of Jerry Lee Lewis during a Million Dollar out-take and I put it all down to Frank's extra-closet religious fervour.

To have believed in the Devil and hell as real things in the way we were supposed to believe in God and heaven as real things would have driven the lot of us insane. To have a strong faith in your own eternal damnation would screw up anybody's head. In music class, when the priest appeared to teach us hymns and songs of love , we would hijack his gentle piano and beat the hell out of it. Hair slicked back, blazer collars up and lips curled, we would hammer a music to satisfy, shake nerves and rattle brains in honest ecstasy. This was surely the madness of sinners who knew in their hearts that they were going straight to hell.

Without a shadow of a doubt!

Uncle James had seen the Devil but we took it as a yarn. He had seen him slipping through the rushes with a big black dog like Caesar Curry and James had taken stock. Satan was a tall dark man in a black coat with a velvet collar and here now was the one and the same Devil himself just as James had described him save for the baldiness of his head. Velvetcollar, James called him, baptised him Velvetcollar in the slow monastic waters of the Erne.

What else did I know of the Devil? Damn all! *Paradise Lost* and the great and long forgotten Miltonic oxymoron. Sympathy for the Devil. The Devil Went down the Georgia. Dante's *Inferno*. Between the Devil and the Deep Blue Sea. The Devil Made Me Do It. Devil Woman. That Old Devil Moon. Devilled eggs. Give the Devil his Due. Talk of the Devil. Devil May Care. Devil-Dodger. Author's Devil. Lawyer's Devil. Devil's Own. Devil Take the Hindmost. Devil's Bones etc etc.

Have you never heard of the attorney-general's devils?

I believe that I have but I am presently unsure as to their exact meaning.

They are the counsel of the Treasury.

I'm as wise as ever.

Sicut sus amarcinum amat?

A pig likes what?

Marjoram.

I'm sorry?

As the Devil likes holy water. In other words, he certainly does not, by the hokey!

Have you any other such wondrous phrases.

I have them by the bucketload. The Devil to pay and no pitch hot!

You mean I am in serious trouble.

I mean that exactly. You have kindled a fire for the Devil, my boy, and you are doing the Devil's own dance!

But I've been yanking the Devil by the tail!

You've been trying to ship the devil around the stump! Go on: tell the truth and shame the Devil!

I need a long spoon if I am to sup with the Devil.

The Devil dances in an empty pocket!

The Devil in Dublin City!

You've hit the nail on the head there, boy! The Devil sick a monk would be!

What am I to do? Simply sit here and beat the Devil's tattoo?

He must go that the Devil drives.

Who said that?

Shakespeare, he of the woollen pipes. All's well that ends well.

Here's hoping.

I emerged from my conscience wrastle to find that the Devil himself was still leering at me with the reddest of eyes.

Don't roll those bloodshot eyes at me, I said under my breath.

Wynonie Harris, he whispered. Why do I have all the best tunes?

There's one we forgot! There y'are now!

The Devil ordered more drink and was greeted warmly by one or two people you might not expect, rock stars mainly but the odd socialite type with no specific talent that you might put your finger on. The Devil was most courteous to everyone and on several occasions sent outrageous rounds of drink to nearby tables.

So about the pipes? You ever get around to learning anything?

I had the odd lesson from Captain James T. Martin of the New York Police Department and there was a given moment when I played every tune in world as a special treat from the Central Park division of the Tuatha Dé Danaan. I also handled a fine set of pipes in the city of Paris – again a gift from the *sí*. These pipes however I did not get around to squeezing.

You were as full as forty badgers I believe, laughed the Devil.

I am invariably as full as forty badgers, I replied.

The Devil locked his hands together as if in prayer and twisted a terrible crack in his neck.

I'm very fond of the pipes myself, he breathed conspiratorially. They are a grand instrument with tremendous possibilities. The chanter, bag and bellows, the regulators and keys: it's so damn complicated! And the music is so very sweet!

I find it hard to believe – if you don't mind me saying so – that you are a connoisseur of the union pipes. You seem far removed from the sheer undiluted purity of Liam Óg Ó Floinn.

The Devil winced.

No further away than you are yourself! he snapped, clearly needled.

But the pipes are wholesome, honourable and pure, I said.

When Ó Floinn plays them yes! he spat, for there is nothing I can do with him! Did you ever see such an immovable object?

Well Ó Floinn is my man, I announced.

Yes but you are no Ó Floinn! You are a class of farm animal and even a pig can play the pipes: I refer you to a sixteenth century manuscript in the Royal Irish Academy. I go there the odd time.

I was wound up.

How dare you refer to me as porcine! You're one to talk! You're a fuckin' goat!

Seirizzim! A bearded ruminant quadruped!

Listen here you to me. I can call you whatever I want and I'll tell you for why. I am a better man than you, as it were, and I have power over you whether you like it or not. You have been dancing on my dime for many a year and you haven't an ounce of grace left to fight me. I can have you whenever I want and I intend to have you very, very soon.

Move it, boy! Hit the road, Jack!

I stared at the Devil and he was an evil bastard right enough.

Listen, he said, as I have outlined, I could have you whenever I want but I'm a reasonable man and I like to do things properly – above board and in a business-like fashion. I propose that a contract is drawn up in the customary manner and you undertake to exchange one soul the property of yourself for one item of recompense which happens to be in my gift. It's very straightforward. I get your soul and you get a little something from me. Fair exchange is no robbery. Now, amn't I a decent spud when you think about it.

Paga-fuckin-ini!

Spot on. I was onto this playboy's game alright. Sell him my soul no less! And after what happened to Robert Johnson – on his knees barking like a dog.

I told the Devil to take himself off.

More power to you!

Do you realise, said the Devil, that you can have anything you want? Take women for instance. How would you like Leonard Cohen's backing vocalists?

Oh, stop it!

Or Cynthia Ní Mhurchú?

Ah now, lads, stop!

What about Cathleen Ni Houlihan – Lady Lavery herself with her elbow perched on a harp?

Oh yes! She's right on the money!

Or that woman in the *Oh Carolina* video?

Don't listen to him!

I wasn't listening to him.

Good man, your da!

The Devil tried again.

What about some financial assistance eh? I could fix it that you win the Lotto ? You would have money to burn and a carwash in your garden.

I don't want your money! I told him, bearing up well.

That's my boy! Take no shit!

I felt terrible. I felt weak, desperate, powerless and lost. The Devil was playing with me like I was a toy. He knew he would get me in the end and I suppose I knew it too.

> Weary is the way, and I'm a weary man tonight –
> Ah, the fairy pipers that awoke me long ago,
> When the mists began to shiver at the coming of
> > the light,
> And the wind was in the heather, soft and low!

> Weary is the way, and I'm a weary man tonight –
> Ah, the fairy pipers that awoke me long ago,
> Still they're calling as they called me when my
> > heart and foot were light,
> And the wind was in the heather, soft and low.

Oh, but that's beautiful! Did you write that yourself?

No. Robertson wrote that.

Who's he when he's at home?

Divil the hate I know!

The Devil knew what I was thinking and he placed his awful hand on top of mine.

What about if I told you that you could play the pipes?

144

That I could give you the finest set of pipes ever made and that you would squeeze from them the greatest music ever heard; that you would be the greatest piper ever to pipe, better than Miss Mollie Morrissey, better than Mr O Farrell, better than Martin O'Reilly, the Blind Piper of Galway . . . better than Liam Óg Ó Floinn?

Oh, by dad, he's got you now!

Indeed and he has. Shame. Shame. Shame. Back at the crossroads I had chosen not to follow the Great Bendy Road of Temptation at the end of which lay the great set of pipes that would make me the greatest piper in the world. I had chosen instead to take my chances on the road known to the Good People as The Great Hard Road. Niamh of the Golden Hair had told me that she knew nothing of that road other than the rumour that it and the Great Bendy Road of Temptation were both felloes of the same circuitous route. She was indeed bang on. Here I was confronted with the very temptation of the pipes themselves – all in exchange for a soul already beyond redemption.

Ah, now, don't be talking like that.

I'm ashamed to say this but I knew this was going to happen. Somewhere inside me I knew that it would come eventually to this. The manner of my life was such that inevitably I would meet whatever it was that was strewing my path with primroses and pleasure. The time had now come, so to speak, to pay the piper, the primrose strewer, Velvetcollar – the Devil himself.

Well, I hope you have prepared yourself, my boy, and stored up the graces for the great Devil wrastle ahead?

I'm afraid that for once you are way off the mark. You make an assumption and your assumption is errant. It is true that I was not listening to the Devil when he tempted me with all the women in the world and all the money in the court of Conor. It is true that these temptations were of little consequence and the awful reason is this.

Once I had more than a man could want – that blissful warm-limbed time when I was in the goosedown bedrooms of Niamh of the Golden Hair deep in the palaces of the Good People. It is also true that I had more than a man could want when I was in the jewelled appartment of Lara Heidsieck, the thief of Paris, beautiful, grey-eyed and tall. It is true that I had more than a man could want when I gargled champagne with my languid companion and a box of strawberries. It is true that I had more than any man could want when I leapt the walls of childhood on the German cruiser while listening to the sounds of a Planxty tape called *The Woman I Loved So Well*. All of the foregoing is fact, true bill and cannot be denied.

I was also unmoved by the Devil's suggestions that I might receive a great set of pipes that would make me the greatest piper ever heard: better than Miss Mollie Morrissey, better than Mister O'Farrell and better than Martin O'Reilly, the Blind Piper of Galway. Even when the Devil said I would even be better than Liam Óg Ó Floinn I found it easy to resist.

Good lad!

Ah but wait till you hear! As I keep telling you – you haven't heard the half of it. The reason I could refuse these invitations is an awful one. What I am about to tell you will prove if proof were needed that we are all evil in the extreme. What you are about to hear is the most shocking example in history of cold and calculated evil, so far from where I was reared and to my everlasting shame.

Sir, I said to the Devil, thank you for your offers and many of them I confess, I find attractive. You, sir, wish to strike a deal with me so that you can have my eternal soul and indeed I care so little for myself that, yes, I am prepared make a deal with you.

What? Have you gone completely doolally?

You came close, I said to the Devil, when you told me that I could play the pipes better than Liam Ó Floinn. That indeed is tempting. But if you are to have my soul you must go just a little further.

Name it, smiled the Devil, his eyes lighting up.

I want more than just to play the pipes like Liam Ó Floinn.

Yes? What? Just name it?

I want, I said solemnly, to *be* Liam Ó Floinn.

Oh, jeepers creepers, mothers and weepers!

I want, I continued, to become Liam Ó Floinn himself – to actually *be* him – to play, look, walk, talk and breathe like Liam Ó Floinn. If I can *become* Liam Ó Floinn then you can have my soul and all belonging to it.

The Devil let go of my hand and suggested that I follow him into a side room away from the main party of revellers. I went with him and entered a room empty but for a rock star who appeared to be in a coma. The Devil stood fornenst me and raised his hand. His eyes blazed red and rivers of drool cascaded from between his blackened teeth. His baldie head perspired and fair gleamed.

I was filled with a terrific excitement and spitting on one of my hands I held it out to the Devil. He spat on his own hand and we shook.

The job's a good'un, he said

Well, this is beyond all!

With that my whole body began to convulse and a terrible shivering clawed through my body and I began to twist and contort. My metamorphosis was brief and soon I was gazing down at my two new piper's hands – the hands of Liam Óg Ó Floinn! In an instant the Devil was gone and I too ran from the club and out onto Grafton Street.

Goodnight Liam, said the bouncer, I don't think I've ever seen you in here before.

It was true! I was Ó Floinn! I ran like a maniac back to my digs in Sandymount and upon entering my bedroom I made straight for the shaving mirror and there to my astonishment was the noble countenance of Liam Óg Ó Floinn – the ace and deuce of pipers! I was Liam Óg Ó Floinn! Olé! Olé! Olé!

As I stood fascinated by my own face I noticed that there was a strange box, like a little coffin, laid out on the bed. As I turned, I knew in my heart what was within and with great ceremonial care I flicked open the catches and opened the lid to find a beautiful set of pipes lying sleeping in a bed of red velvet. I took them out piece by piece and as I trembled with excitement and anticipation I began to assemble them around me, slipping my elbows through leather and sliding the bellows up my arm. I, at last, was Liam Óg Ó Floinn!

This is scandalous – and your mother on her two knees doing the perpetual novena!

Much like the night in Central Park only better, a great music began to swirl around me. The pipes began to sound and they were my fingers that were drawing the tunes! My elbows that were squeezing the air! My foot that was gravely tapping and my honourable face, solid and decent, which sat perfectly above all! There was no manic rocking from side to side, no octopus wrestling – only the noble, stoical, concentration that is Ó Floinn himself!

How can you face yourself in the mirror?

I'm sorry do I know you? My name's Ó Floinn. I think you've got the wrong man.

Well, where are you yourself?

Me, myself, I? Damned if I know. Would you like to hear me play 'The Woman I Never Forgot', 'The Pullet' and 'The Ladies' Pantalettes'?

I hope you're happy now!

As the day is long!

I rang Christy and we talked for hours.

TWENTY

I remained as Liam Óg Ó Floinn for the guts of a year. For
legal reasons I cannot tell you about everything that
happened. As you will appreciate it would involve highly
complicated and expensive principles of law should the wrong
thing be said. I shall however tell you as much as I can.

For an entire year I toured the world as Liam Ó Floinn. I
was within his body and played the pipes just as the great man
himself. Perhaps you have seen me perform? That night in the
Duke of York with Arty McGlynn, that was me! That big night
in the National Concert Hall, that was me! In fact any time
you might have seen Liam Óg Ó Floinn during this period it
was, truth be told, me.

What happened to Liam Óg Ó Floinn is, I'm afraid, beyond
my ken. I can only assume that he became me in a straight
swap. This was of course unfortunate for the piper because it
must have been a considerable trauma to find himself with
talentless fingers and a less than noble countenance. I cannot
be sure of this theory but I did once overhear a conversation
about me boking in Bob Dylan's caravan at a rock festival in
Tramore in the county of Waterford. Needless to say, I was
nowhere near the place. I was in fact on stage that very night
in Stuttgart, Germany, performing *The Brendan Voyage* with
full orchestra.

I was for once welcome in Baggot Street bars and people

were happy to stand near me and, what's more, stand me a drink. I would be quite content most evenings but occasionally there was the odd disquieting snippet of information and a modicum of guilt might slightly prick what was left of my conscience.

Do you remember that fella from the north that used to throw up all over the place? He was some boy! Have any of yis seen him lately?

And then the garbled information: sightings in the counties of Monaghan and Cork. Boking episodes on Aranmore Island, the Slieve Russell Hotel, Rostrevor in the county of Down, Matt's of Westport in the county of Mayo and Newbridge in the county of Kildare. At such moments I suffered confusion and brief moments of deep sympathy for the once godlike Ó Floinn at whose feet I used to sit and weep.

Concern for my own soul was at times minimal. I was up to my oxters in league with the Devil and there was no possible gloss to be put upon it. *Si peccasse negamus, fallimur, et nulla est in nobis veritas.*

Oh that's clever! Some chance of your denying your sin now! Leave this execrable art!

My heart's so harden'd, I cannot repent:

Scarce can I name salvation, faith, or heaven,

In any case, I had gigs to do, guest appearances to make – the Everly Brothers – all sorts of people. Man but I could rattle out the tunes! Every tune in the world! Bellows and bag, chanter and drones: laments, marches, hornpipes, slip-jigs, jigs and reels – the whole caboodle on the *Dudelsack*!

The Devil left me to my own devices. After all he had what he wanted. He had my soul and when the time came I would become his companion prince in hell. This was not something

I looked forward to particularly but as long as I could play 'The Foxhunters' in the way that I could I would keep all thoughts of eternal damnation on the long finger.

You're a big old country fool! The Devil's business is bad business and in your neo-Faustian quest for piping excellence you have brought upon yourself considerable sin. Murder, robbery, bad language, drinking, smoking, snorting, brawling, door-knocking, woman-fondling, necromantic constraint, criminal damage, religion-bashing, not keeping the sabbath day, coveting thy neighbour's pipes and entering a bargain with the Devil himself! Have you no shame?

No.

Have you no fear?

Yes.

Then repent!

Let me play for you now a set of tunes I learned from the playing of Seamus Ennis.

You're a lost cause. He'll be back for you and then we'll see who's the big man!

I confess that at certain post-gig moments such fears did enter my sick mind. There was always something dark that droned around me like the pipes themselves – Robert Johnson on his knees barking like a dog – the corpse of Paganini being passed from devotee to devotee because no clergyman would bury him. All so he could play his caprices on the one string. Yes I knew that the Devil would be back and I knew that when he did come back, I was in for something serious.

Late at night I would lie awake and sweating, wondering what sort of torture the Devil had planned for me. What was hell like? Was it fire and brimstone? Or was it all within ourselves? All I knew was that I knew nothing except that for me it was unavoidable and it would serve me right to suffer. In the meantime, however, I was comfortable, the greatest piper in Ireland and never a boke.

As I have already indicated, I remained as Liam Óg Ó Floinn for the best part of a year. At the end of that year the Devil, as predicated, came back. I was in the county of Donegal doing a low-key gig on the back of a lorry in the town of Dungloe. I was accompanied by a cellist, a violinist, a guitarist and a large man in cattle-dealer boots who rolled out the odd song. It was a grand gig although the position of the lorry in the main street was less than suitable. We were in the middle of a set of tunes which have no names when I chanced to lift my eyes from the space immediately beyond my knees and there he was!

There amid the crowd of mammies and daddies and poke-eating weans was the baldie head of the Prince of Darkness, still wearing the black coat with the velvet collar. His red, bloodshot eyes were upon me and he moved to a standing position right at my feet. He listened intently and applauded loudly throughout, never for a minute taking his eyes off me and letting out the appropriate gulder and whelp at moments of modulation. My playing suffered greatly as a result.

When the show was over and people began to straggle off to chip shops and slot machines, I turned away and began to pack away the pipes. I prayed that when I looked up again, he would be gone.

Not a snowball's.

You're right. His awful bony hand rested once more upon my shoulder.

Grand performance, he said.

A terrible damp sweat broke on the back of my neck and an empty sickness floated in my gut. He leaned over and whispered in my ear those words:

It's time.

Bugger off you big, bad, bald bastard! I shouted.

C'mon son, he said, smoothly, we've made a deal. As far as you go, I've got exclusive rights.

I protested eloquently, even invoking some half-baked principles of contract law, but he was having none of it.

I'll only tell you once more, he warned, if you refuse you'll be very sorry indeed.

G'way and shite!

At the very instant of that vulgar utterance I felt a shivering change occur inside me. I suddenly began to contort and slowly and painfully I regained my old undignified, ignoble and talentless shape. I became myself again. It was horrible! I looked at my hands – the fingers that couldn't play for toffee and I looked at the Devil in all his vile and anagrammatic evil ugliness. I felt that old familiar welling boke.

Just like that day in front of Joseph Haverty's 'Blind Piper' in the National Gallery of Ireland, Merrion Square West, Dublin 2, I felt a sudden dig in ribs, and then another and another. I clutched my side and looked up at the Devil and saw that his blazing eyes were laughing madly. Another elbow in the ribs and I felt the boke rising. I understood at that moment that it was the Devil himself who was beating me about and that it was the Devil himself who was that unseen force that had punched and beaten those awful bokes out of me – manifestations of corruption and foul-smelling evil.

What happened next was most extraordinary. I opened my mouth to spew and nothing came out. I looked at the Devil and again nothing came out – just a terrible boking silence. My face twisted, my mouth gaped, every sinew in my neck strained and every organ in my body seemed about the explode when suddenly from the back of my throat there came a noise. Another dig in the ribs and another noise. It was the noise of the uilleann pipes! A vile and horrible long-note came spurting from my mouth and then more notes until finally a whole tune and all the time my ribs were being punched and the air was flying up out of me and this class of hellish hornpipe was coming like a host of demons from my ears, nose and throat!

I looked up at the Devil and implored him to stop. He smiled quietly.

There you are now. A minute ago you were Liam Óg Ó Floinn; now you are a set of pipes! What you might call the Devil's instrument, eh?

And where does that leave you?

Well, now I'll tell you the whole of it. Here is the awful truth. I am now a set of union or uilleann pipes – here to be played upon by the Devil himself. He keeps me under a rock on the Atlantic coast and whenever he takes the notion, he take me out and puts me under his oxter. I hang there on his lap like a limp rag doll and he squeezes and thumps and pokes and prods the living daylights out of me. He plays awful, terrible, out-of-tune lamentations which I boke up out of my tortured throat and he laughs away to himself. Sometimes, for sheer badness, he holds my nose.

So if, of an evening, you're walking along the Donegal coast and you hear the hellish sound of uilleann pipes in the wind, think of me. For it is not the sound of the *sí* . It is the sound of this lost soul – a set of pipes played upon by the Devil himself.

Take care, yourselves, never to smoke Twenty Regal Kingsize one after the other, to avoid twelve pints of stout at the one sitting and to ignore any tourists you meet in the men's toilets.

Take care also never to fall for fairy women, boke from great heights or attend Dublin nightclubs. Stay sober in the Vatican and always listen to your mother and St Augustine's mother and never eat strawberries with a languid companion. Steer clear of northern writers. Never go into heroic warp spasm if you can help it, abstain from the slaughter of schoolteachers and do not take musical instruments not belonging to you. Above all, I counsel you in this, never get obsessed with pipers, never make a deal with a man in a long black coat with a velvet collar and be very very careful where you boke – it might come back in your face.